E-MAIL

STEPHEN A. CASWELL

Artech House
Boston · London

© 1988
Gage Educational Publishing Company
A Division of Canada Publishing Corporation

Printed in Canada
92 91 90 89 88 5 4 3 2 1

ISBN 0-89006-303-6

The **Converging Technologies Series** is designed to help today's managers lead and control the profound technological tide now sweeping the traditional workplace; dramatically improve organizational performance; and improve the quality of work life. Under the Consulting Editorship of Don Tapscott, an international authority in the field of integrated office systems, the Converging Technologies Series draws on the proven experience and insights of industry experts.

Other books in this series:

The Information Edge

People and Productivity: A Manager's Guide to Ergonomics in the Electronic Office

The Ergonomics Payoff: Designing the Electronic Office

The Human Imperative: Planning for People in the Electronic Office

Planning for Integrated Office Systems: A Strategic Approach

Contents

Chapter 5   Telematic Services   67

Chapter 6   Computer Message Systems   81

Chapter 7   CBMS Services and Systems   109

Foreword

No one living in the 1980s needs to be told that advances in computer and telecommunications technologies are changing the way we live our lives. The signs are all around us. This book deals with one particular product of the merging of computers and telecommunications — electronic mail. While electronic mail has been around since the 1840s with Samuel Morse's telegraph and Alexander Bain's facsimile machine, only one or two million people worldwide had ever touched an electronic mail system directly as late as the mid-1970s. Since then, digital facsimile machines, personal computers, and computer mailbox systems have allowed electronic mail to be used by millions of people directly. The Electronic Mail Association estimates that there are already five million people using computer mailbox systems in North America alone. And all indications are that this number will double or triple in just a few years.

Because of the rapid growth of electronic mail, there is a strong need for a book that focuses on the benefits, applications, operational characteristics, and implementation requirements of electronic mail. *E-Mail* by Steve Caswell is such a book. It will be of value to top executives and corporate planners who are evaluating e-mail's strategic benefits; to line managers who want to implement electronic mail systems within their individual departments or sections; to people within those departments who want to know more about electronic mail; and to the sales forces and other employees in vendor organizations who are selling one type of electronic mail system and want to broaden their knowledge of the overall industry.

One question that should be considered when evaluating the implementation of any new technology, particularly at a time when we see such a dazzling array of "dramatic innovations", is whether or not that technology is destined to gain wide acceptance. In the case of electronic mail, as Caswell demonstrates, the obvious advantages over present-day communications systems ensure that the growth will be dramatic. What's more, the evolution of accepted international standards for electronic messaging is proceeding at a surprisingly rapid pace. X.400, the international standard that connects mail systems from multiple vendors, is indeed the "white knight" of the industry, as Caswell points out.

Now, it is true that some futurists predicted six or seven years ago that everyone in our society would be using electronic mail by 1987 because it was such a wonderful technology. It is a great technology, but the history of innovation demonstrates that new ways of doing things always take some time to gain universal acceptance. In 1935, for example, the aircraft that was to revolutionize the travel industry, the DC-3, made its debut. Savvy observers predicted that the new planes and their successors would replace intercity passenger rail travel, and they did — but not before the railroad industry set all-time records for passenger usage in the late 1940s and early 1950s. Similarly, the technology of television, invented in the mid-1920s, found little acceptance for a full twenty years after its first demonstration, but dramatic, unprecedented increases in the sales of television sets in 1947 and 1948 quickly turned the television into a central element of our modern society (for better or worse).

Although electronic mail and messaging technology, including the related applications of order entry, electronic data interchange, etc., is bursting dramatically onto the national scene today, and promises to gain virtually universal usage in offices and factories and eventually in homes as well, it too will take time. This, of course, can be frustrating to people who have grown up in an age of instant gratification, but we should all keep in mind that e-mail is one of the fastest growing communications technologies in man's history, with a growth rate that continues to accelerate.

My final comments are about the author. Steve Caswell is certainly the appropriate person to write this book. His thoughtful insights have been read, considered, and debated by virtually everyone of note in the electronic mail industry over the past twelve years. While some analysts have been satisfied with producing relatively unimaginative industry facts and figures, Steve has probed and challenged and confronted the central issues facing the industry in his writings for *EMMS* newsletter, in his multi-client research studies, and in his consulting work. The readers of this book will benefit from his extensive experience and knowledge, and, particularly, from his strategic insights.

Michael F. Cavanagh
Executive Director
Electronic Mail Association

Preface

It is very easy to view electronic mail as a narrow industry, with its vendors concerned with turning a profit and its users concerned with delivering messages. Electronic mail, however, has a long-term impact that is far broader. Because electronic mail adds regularity to our telecommunications network, it makes a critical contribution to our evolving system of global communications, which is a necessary component for the evolution of mankind. In this context, developing electronic mail systems is a noble pursuit.

It is a strange notion, perhaps, to think of developing electronic mail systems as connected to the greater good of mankind. Nevertheless, I believe that it is true. Mankind's evolution requires more than kindly sentiments on everyone's part. It requires a practical infrastructure that will allow the complex needs of five billion people to be met on a day-to-day basis.

This book is one small contribution to the development of the e-mail industry. It is one result of the twelve years I have spent as a researcher, writer, and consultant in electronic mail and office automation. During this period, I've had the privilege of meeting and speaking with thousands of people in these industries around the world. For this reason, there is no way that I can thank everyone personally for the contributions that they have made to my work.

I would like to acknowledge a number of people who have played important roles. Don Tapscott, the editor of the Converging Technologies Series, asked me to write this book and deserves special thanks. Vinton Cerf, Richard Coughenour, and several unnamed people also deserve a special thanks for the time they spent in reviewing the first draft and providing me with excellent comments. I would also like to give special thanks to Ken Bosomworth, who is the president of International Resource Development, which publishes *EMMS*. Without Ken's support since 1975, I would never have learned enough about this industry to be able to write a book about it.

I would also like to thank Mike Cavanagh, Steve Kirchoff, Walter Ulrich, Steve Glagow, Tony Caplin, George Brandes, Lou Galterio, John Geraghty, and the other members of the Electronic Mail Association for all the help they have given me in understanding our industry. In addition, I would like to thank Ted Myer and Ian Cunningham for sharing their insights on X.400 over the years, along with Bob and Marilyn Harcharik, N. Dean Meyer, Charan Lohara, Al Law, Jack Griffin, Larry Brilliant, Erik Arnum, Gordon Thompson, David Whitten, Dick Derosier, Harry Stevens, and Mike Myers for sharing their general knowledge. There are numerous others who have contributed to my knowledge of the industry. I wish I could mention them all and hope they will understand my oversight.

I would also like to thank Julia Woods, Joan Homewood and the team at Gage for their help in putting the book together. Gage has supported me in my efforts to learn about desktop publishing from the ground up. The book was delivered to Gage formatted for typesetting using an Apple Macintosh. I would also like to thank Lora Lee Johnson for a final editing pass.

I would like to thank my wife, Veronica, and our children, Alex and Laila, for their patience and understanding while the book was being written. I would particularly like to acknowledge my father, Jack Caswell, who passed away while the book was in draft form. He would have been proud to see it in print. I would also like to acknowledge the many teachers who helped me to get an education, especially Hugo Bedau from Tufts University. We often forget our education. Without it, however, this book and my career would not be possible.

Finally, I'd like to apologize to my mother's friends and neighbors, and ask their indulgence. It is, after all, a mother's right to be a bit proud of a son's accomplishments. Please don't let her overdo it though.

The Challenge

Knowledge is power. It is a truism that has been known for thousands of years. During the past 10 years, computing and communications technologies have opened the doors to systems that can bring an unprecedented flow of knowledge—and a new level of power—to organizations. At the end of this technological rainbow is a pot of gold: *a competitive edge*. Business, after all, is a competitive experience with success going to those who best serve their customers' needs.

The Networking Challenge

As more and more people study how best to employ technology in today's business climate, no single technology is emerging as the key that will unlock the power of information systems. Instead, the key to power will come through the integration of a series of technologies into powerful networks of machines and people.

Although the networks and the technologies that create them are quite complex, the implications are very simple. *Advanced information networks will magnify the ability of people to store, gather, prepare, and communicate important information.* The challenge, which extends to both top executives and mid-level managers, is to cut through the complexity of the myriad technologies on the market and mold them into a unified, integrated network that serves the people who use them.

The Power of Electronic Mail

The topic of this book is one of the major technologies of any network—electronic mail. Like networking itself, electronic mail is an ambiguous term. Although electronic mail is a generic term familiar to most people in the business community, it is not easy to define. Here is the definition adopted by the Electronic Mail Association (EMA) after many months of deliberation:

> Electronic mail is the generic name for non-interactive communication of text, data, image or voice messages between a sender and designated recipients by systems utilizing telecommunications links.

The definition is typical of most high tech definitions: in its efforts to capture the technical element, it somehow misses the human element. Although the heart of electronic mail may be non-interactive communications, its soul is people communicating with people, whether it be directly or via their machine agents. When viewed in this light, the benefits of electronic mail are simple to understand: information that once took 24 hours or more to be delivered with little control over its time of delivery can now be delivered in minutes and at a specified time for its maximum impact. This allows people to respond faster and with more precision in all aspects of their work.

User experiences with electronic mail show clearly how the technology can help people do their jobs better. During the past few years, for example, businesses in North America have given computerized mailboxes to a few million of their employees. Companies whose top management has adopted electronic mail and related office automation technologies have reported some dramatic stories where electronic mail has given them a competitive edge.

The Competitive Edge

To cite one example, Beneficial Finance Corp.'s top executives, board of directors, key consultants, and legal planners all participate in the company's electronic mail network, based on Data General CEO systems. On a Friday in 1985, the day before Labor Day, Beneficial's top executives were surprised by multiple offers for the firm's Western Auto subsidiary. The problem was that the offers were only valid until the close of business on the following Wednesday. Because of the holiday weekend, the company had two business days to reach a decision worth tens of millions of dollars.

Although Beneficial would have reached a decision on the offers without using electronic mail, the system was critical in providing planners with the best information possible. During the weekend and holiday, Beneficial's key players were in constant touch via electronic mail— passing around information on the proposals, along with the financial and operations data required to make the decision. When the board met the following week, it was prepared to deal with the key business issues involved, rather than having to spend hours in tedious background meetings before tackling the key issues. In looking back on the experience, Frank Caspersen, Beneficial's CEO, said that using electronic mail gave his firm a decision-making edge in the market.[1]

The Operational Edge and Resistance

When key executives use electronic mail, they have an edge in passing around critical information. Electronic mail, however, is a technology that is useful at every level of operation in a company because it reduces the "information float" (the time in which information is in transit), which allows people and companies to respond faster when the information is critical to the decisions that must be made.

Despite the growing number of success stories and the obvious benefits of electronic mail, however, there is still considerable resistance to the technology, especially from people who are unfamiliar with its benefits and are afraid that its costs cannot be properly controlled. Although this type of resistance is breaking down rapidly, it clearly indicates, nevertheless, that people are the final arbiters of whether or not to use a new technology. Thus, the job of planning and implementing electronic mail is as much related to educating users about its benefits and setting up systems to properly control usage, as it is to implementing systems technically.

The Challenge to Top Executives

Electronic mail— and its related office automation technologies— poses a challenge to top executives, who must lead the way in understanding and implementing the technology effectively. Top executives are challenged by:

- Changing ingrained habits that have been formed over decades;

- Providing leadership to mid-level managers who will plan and implement electronic mail;

- Developing the proper organizational structure required to implement electronic mail and related technologies;

- Understanding the organizational importance of the X.400 Standard now entering the market;

- Understanding the financial relationships of advanced technologies; and

- Developing rational systems for evaluating continued investment in new technologies.

Changing Ingrained Habits

The challenge to top executives should not be underestimated as there are numerous pitfalls along the way—the toughest ones being psychological and social. Most top executives reached their present position by dealing with people and financial or market-related problems. Until recently, information technologies (IT) have largely been ignored at the top of organizations, with mid-level managers taking the lead in implementing IT for cost-cutting purposes.

Although many of today's top executives recognize that technologies such as electronic mail are strategic to their companies' long-term development, they still find it hard to change their own habits. Keyboards, personal computers, and new communications media are alien to most top executives, who have spent the last 10 to 20 years in a non-automated environment.

The purpose here is not to convince top executives to start pecking away at keyboards, but to point out the subtle pitfall that can come from not wanting to change. The best way to point it out is through an existing situation: There are a number of electronic mail executives who refuse to use their own systems even though they believe in the technology enough to run companies that sell it. Every time they are asked why they do not use the technology, they make lame excuses. They never unveil the real reason—fear of change. In one instance, a new president took over from a CEO who used his own system extensively for executive communications. The system was being used about 80 hours per month by the company's top 12 executives. In a matter of weeks, however, use of the system virtually dried up and the company went back to paper memos.[2]

Because top executives must provide leadership to their organization, understanding that people fear change is a critical insight. Through self-analysis, they must decide if their fear is rational or a general fear of change. If it is the latter, they must design strategies to overcome it.

Providing Leadership

Management is the art of leadership. Most top executives understand this intuitively. In the past, they have allowed specialists to take the leadership role in information technologies. Although this was sufficient when IT was restricted, this role must change now that information technologies have become critical factors in key management and professional jobs in most organizations.

Top executives must educate themselves as to the benefits of technology so they can make key decisions about its implementation. There can be no shortcut. This does not mean that top executives must take crash courses in using computers, learning all of the intricate details and buzzwords of computing and communications. It means that they must take the time to learn the benefits of technology and understand the financial implications to their organizations.

In electronic mail, for example, top executives do not have to be direct users on a daily basis to obtain the benefits, although this would be exemplary. At a minimum, they must make certain that they understand the benefits of electronic mail and that their support staffs in key positions take advantage of it on a daily basis. They should also know how to use electronic mail during emergencies, when their support staff may not be available.

Developing the Proper Organizational Structure

During the past decade, responsibility for implementing advanced information technologies has diffused throughout most organizations. The Management Information Systems (MIS) department is responsible for large computers. The telecommunications department is responsible for telephones. The word processing center is responsible for word processing. The information center is responsible for personal computing. This diffusion of responsibility is particularly unwieldy in electronic mail, which incorporates seven different technologies. It is quite common, for example, to have multiple electronic mail systems running inside an organization, with no single group responsible for overall planning. As an example, Citibank recently had six different computer mailbox systems in operation, along with separate telex and facsimile networks.

One of the most important tasks facing top executives is the design of an organizational structure so that planning can proceed properly. This does not mean that planning for electronic mail should automatically be centralized, however, and that all duplicate systems should be abolished in favor of one corporate system.

In *Competing In Time*, a book on using telecommunications to gain a competitive advantage in the market, the author, Dr. Peter Keen, compares Citibank, with its multiple systems, to Manufacturers Hanovers Trust, whose network is highly centralized as a result of top-down planning. According to Keen, Manufacturers Hanovers' network "was, and is far better designed and cost effective than Citibank's worldwide communications network." Nevertheless, Keen also says that, because Citibank's different systems were often set up directly by their users, overall usage was higher than in Manufacturers Hanovers' more elegant network. Keen is pointing out the reality that giving people a direct stake in planning their own systems is often far more important to usage than design elegance and cost-effectiveness.[3]

It is precisely because of contrary factors, such as centralization versus decentralization, that top executives must take a leadership role in setting up the appropriate organizational structure for implementing electronic mail and other advanced technologies. Who but they can strike the right balance for their companies?

Understanding the Importance of the X.400 Standard

Communication standards are often viewed as boring technical details that are of interest only to engineers. In electronic mail, however, the reverse is the case. In 1984, the X.400 Standard was adopted by the International Telecommunications Union as a means of interconnecting electronic mail systems from different manufacturers. The Standard was designed for use by both public and private mail networks.

Although top executives do not have to understand the intricate details of the X.400 Standard, they must understand its implications for planning and implementing electronic mail systems. Because X.400 allows mail systems from multiple vendors to communicate, it opens up the ability to allow decentralized planning without creating a Tower of Babel inside the organization. Thus, X.400 is more than a technical standard. It is an important tool for allowing organizations to define their own *modus operandi* in planning and implementing electronic mail.

Understanding Financial Relationships

What does it mean to have every top executive involved in implementing technology? They do not have to understand the intricate details of advanced technologies, for example, any more than they must understand the intricate details of how every aspect of their organization operates. They must, however, understand the benefits of advanced technologies and their financial relationships; otherwise, they should not be top executives. Most businesses, for example, have developed detailed financial ratios to understand their performance in relationship to competition. Although top executives may understand the intricate details of only one aspect of the organization, they all understand the key financial indicators of overall performance.

Here is where top executives can make a critical difference in implementing advanced technologies. Key technology planners, for example, may understand the technologies but often do not have enough insight to understand their relationship to other critical operational indicators. Furthermore, because responsibility for advanced technologies is diffused, few organizations even know how much they are spending for all of their advanced information technologies. At this writing, for example, basic statistics rarely exist to indicate how much an organization is investing in information technologies, let alone whether or not it is too much or too little. Top executives must bring together a multidisciplinary team of players to create the required indicators; otherwise, the organization will be flying blind.

Developing Rational Systems of Evaluation

In the long run, the greatest challenges that face top executives are developing rational systems for investing in advanced information technologies and monitoring their performance. Electronic mail, for example, cannot be cost-justified to the penny any more than the telephone or a new factory. There are also no generally accepted statistics or financial ratios that tell how much companies across different industries do or should invest in electronic mail.

In this vacuum, how can management make rational decisions about investing in electronic mail? Initially, top executives must rely on both common sense and the operational statistics that do exist. For electronic mail, this means understanding the investment that is required, along with the potential payback, so that a considered decision can be made concerning the risk involved. It is also important to make certain that usage is monitored so that the company— and the industry— has a chance to develop proper operational statistics and industry averages.

Summary

Taking advantage of electronic mail is a challenge to top executives. The first step in meeting the challenge is committing time to investigate the benefits. Top executives can no longer afford to abrogate this responsibility. Once they become sufficiently aware, they are then faced with making a decision whether or not to invest in electronic mail systems and networks. As no operating statistics or industry averages exist that say how much is a sufficient investment, top executives must use their common sense to make the decision. Common sense means that:

- Planning should be coordinated throughout the organization;
- Investments should have a reasonable payback period;
- Systems should be established to monitor performance; and
- Rational indicators and controls should be developed to determine continued investment and operational parameters.

The Challenge to Planners

After top executives meet the challenge, those charged with planning and implementing electronic mail have a challenge of their own: How do they develop their electronic mail technology effectively during the next decade?

If there were only one electronic mail technology and if the world were rational, then the process would be simple. Unfortunately, there are seven different electronic mail technologies, and the world is anything but rational. Not only must planners cope with the technical issues associated with the implementation of electronic mail across a diverse user base, but they must also face diverse non-technical issues such as resistance to change from some users and resistance to centralized planning from others.

There are seven challenges for electronic mail planners. Each one will have an impact on the choices that planners make during the next few years. The seven challenges are:

- Developing a proper investment framework;
- Overcoming resistance to change;
- Protecting the system's effectiveness;
- Implementing intelligent, electronic user agents;
- Evolving today's systems into networks;
- Integrating all non-interactive traffic; and
- Developing strategic applications.

Developing a Proper Investment Framework

Electronic mail has numerous benefits, which are discussed in detail in the next chapter. Understanding the benefits, however, is only half of the equation. Management must still decide how much to invest to realize the benefits. Here is where the problem lies because it is extremely difficult to put a quantified value on electronic mail. There are too many variables involved.

Although top executives must sanction and support a reasonable investment structure, planners must develop the structure. Fortunately, organizations have a number of precedents to help them reach a decision. The telephone, for example, has no quantifiable value as to its benefits, except for very specific applications such as dunning, yet organizations still distribute phones to every office worker. The reason is that common sense has shown us that the telephone is worth the investment, and companies have developed an acceptable cost structure.

How much does a company invest in telephone communications? The answer is typically about $700 to $1,000 (U.S.) in capital per employee. In addition, businesses spend about $100 to $200 per employee per month for operations, including outside phone lines and long distance charges.[4] If the company could estimate the worth of electronic mail in relation to that of the telephone, it would be a good starting place to evaluate how much to spend on electronic mail and how to structure the investment.

Overcoming Resistance to Change

There are many people who will debate using electronic mail on logical issues, such as its cost justification or its inherent usefulness, to hide their real bias: they do not want to change or they are afraid that electronic mail will threaten their power within the organization. From this perspective, all of the logic that can be brought to bear either for or against electronic mail is almost irrelevant. If a potential user does not want to change habits or has private fears for his job, no study will persuade this person to use electronic mail. Any strategy to implement electronic mail within an organization must take this reality into account. The factor is so important that it will impact every theoretical implementation rate that is based on logical factors, such as cost, availability of terminals, identifiable applications, etc.

This is also the toughest factor to deal with because it defies logic. People who will not change their habits will say almost anything that makes sense (to them) to resist changing. Developing electronic mail throughout the organization and using it strategically has as much to do with dealing with these people as any other single factor.

This problem adds to the cost of electronic mail above the cost of hardware, software, and basic training. Planners must anticipate encountering pockets of resistance from influential employees and must develop proper strategies to overcome them. It makes no sense, for example, to use intimidation to force people to change. On the other hand, if an organization can gain a competitive advantage in the market, it makes no sense to lose it because a few influential employees have some hidden fears of change. Diplomacy is required.

Protecting the System's Effectiveness

Electronic mail has to perform some function for society in order for it to have any value. One main function is to add an element of effectiveness to electronic communications that is not obtainable by the telephone. Communication, according to basic theory, consists of a sender, a receiver, a message, and feedback. The telephone has all these elements. Unfortunately, the telephone is not particularly effective—you can only rely on it for so much. First, one common truth of modern society is that most telephone calls do not reach their recipients because they are away from their phones. Although the estimates vary, it is safe to say that 50 to 70 percent of calls are not completed. This, of course, gives rise to "telephone tag"—the recipient returns the call only to find that the sender is not available, and on it goes.

Second, when the call is completed, the message itself may be garbled. The telephone is a "hot" medium that allows a lot of feedback in relationship to the message, which has an impact on the effectiveness of the call. During the feedback process, for example, the intended message may not be fully delivered or some key points may be forgotten.

Electronic mail has the same four elements—sender, receiver, message, and feedback—but they are in very different relationship. The sender can estimate to a high degree when the message will be received. A telex, for example, will usually reach the recipient on the same day it is sent, as will an electronic mailbox message. All that is required is that the sender know that the recipient looks for such messages. The content, furthermore, is not open to discussion. It is stored and reproduced with a high degree of accuracy. Although it is subject to varying interpretations, it is possible to ask specifically what one meant by referring to the exact words. Electronic mail, in comparison to the telephone, is a "cool" medium with a low level of feedback that does not intrude into the content of the messages. As delivery of the information can also be stored for the recipient, independent of time and location, this makes electronic mail a highly effective communications medium in comparison to the telephone.

The effectiveness of electronic mail, however, is dependent upon the willingness of people to use the system. If a company installs the technology throughout its organization, for example, only to discover that 30 percent of users never check their mailboxes, then its effectiveness is threatened. To give one example, in April 1986, a small software manufacturer sent out press releases to 120 editors and reporters using MCI Mail, a popular public computer mailbox service. After one month, only 16 of the recipients had checked their mailboxes and read the release. Planners must take this issue into account in order to protect the effectiveness of the system.

Implementing Intelligent, Electronic User Agents

An electronic user agent is a program that runs within an electronic mail system or personal computer and performs tasks in the name of the user. Although simple user agents are preprogrammed by system suppliers to perform tasks such as keeping an inbox of messages, sophisticated agents can perform user-programmed tasks, such as calling other mail systems or data bases and checking for specific messages or facts, and then taking appropriate actions based on the result. It is possible, for example, for a user agent to monitor foreign currency exchanges worldwide on a regular basis, say every 30 minutes, to compare the buying and selling rates of a specific currency and to notify its user whenever specific currencies reach a certain rate or fall outside specified limits. It is also possible to have user agents monitor news wires for specific key words and notify its user whenever these key words are encountered. The user, of course, learns about news stories hours before they appear in print.

The two examples demonstrate the power of the user-agent concept. At present, user agents are typically simple, with most agents programmed by system suppliers to provide basic inbox-outbox and editing functions. The personal computer (PC), however, has already opened the door to advanced user agents with powerful macro languages that can be programmed to perform sophisticated tasks. Developing appropriate user agents for the company will almost certainly be one of the key electronic mail planning functions over the next few years.

Evolving Today's Systems into Networks

Electronic mail is now spreading rapidly throughout industrial nations worldwide. Nevertheless, in most large companies, electronic mail is still implemented as a series of different systems, with each system serving a separate group of users. A major trend in electronic mail is to evolve those separate systems into an integrated network, which has two implications for planners. The first is connecting the different electronic mail technologies together so that messages can be exchanged across different systems. The second implication is far more subtle: evolving systems into networks.

Connecting mail systems together conceptually is well understood by most people in the field and is the subject of intensive standardization efforts. Most vendors have already announced their support for the X.400 Standard and are actively implementing X.400 systems and gateways. IBM has also announced an interconnection strategy via Distributed Office Support System (DISOSS), System Network Architecture Distribution Services (SNADS), and support for X.400 via a gateway. Thus, although interconnection is a problem for many of the smaller vendors in the market, the market leaders have all gone a long way toward allowing their systems to exchange messages.

A more subtle, but equally important, issue is evolving systems into a cohesive network, which is shown in detail in the case study of Digital Equipment in Chapter 12. Digital discovered that even if systems can interconnect, it does not mean that they can be managed properly. As a result, Digital has developed a complete message handling network that solves problems such as supporting a distributed directory of users across the systems they connect. Digital has also dealt with issues such as managing an electronic mail network from a central point and collecting aggregate usage statistics across every node in the network. Because many of the systems on the market have not dealt with the issue of generating adequate usage statistics on one host, it is easy to see the magnitude of the problem to generate such statistics across different systems on a network.

Although the CCITT (International Telephone & Telegraph Consultative Committee), the standards setting body of the International Telecommunications Union that developed X.400, is dealing with the issues of decentralized directories and applications-level network management, standards have yet to be finalized and implementations are non-existent, except in experimental laboratories. The lack of such tools, of course, makes it all the more difficult to establish standardized operating controls over electronic mail networks and poses an enormous short-term problem for planners.

Integrating All Non-Interactive Traffic

Although people-to-people communication distinguishes electronic mail from data processing technologies, non-interactive operation distinguishes electronic mail from other communications technologies, particularly the telephone. Non-interactive traffic can have a time delay from its transmission to its delivery without having an impact on the value of the information. Most companies have a growing amount of electronic non-interactive traffic within their organizations, including Electronic Data Interchange (EDI), which is invoices, purchase orders, and other trade documents sent between companies; internal electronic business forms— including expense reports, requisition forms, or engineering change orders; and batch data processing, such as orders, inventory, or other accounting data. All of this non-interactive traffic can be carried over the same network as people-to-people electronic mail. Integrating all this traffic over one network is part of the challenge of evolving from separate systems into a single network.

Developing Strategic Applications

Although many of the interconnection and networking challenges that face planners today are often out of their control because the solutions have not yet been implemented by vendors, there is one challenge that planners can control: developing strategic applications.

A strategic application is one that improves the company's position in the marketplace either by reducing operating costs or by improving communications with key suppliers, dealers, distributors, and customers. Electronic mail is particularly suited to such applications because of its ability to improve communications, which can translate into improved service and customer satisfaction.

To give one example of a strategic application, Chrysler recently implemented an electronic mail system to improve communications amongst its central headquarters, regional zones, district managers, and dealers. Chrysler's sales operations are organized into five regional zones. District managers, who are basically salespeople who serve dealers, work within each zone and are responsible for about 20 dealers. Before using electronic mail, dealer communications would flow to district managers for some issues, such as ordering cars, and directly to corporate headquarters for other issues, such as tracking orders or dealing with service problems. Because of telephone tag problems, however, it was often difficult for dealers to reach district managers. Furthermore, district managers were often unaware of communications from dealers to corporate headquarters, which were handled via voice communications. Electronic mail was used only by managers at corporate headquarters and the regional zones via a PROFs system from IBM that operated internally.

Chrysler created a complete network by building an interconnection between its internal PROFs system and the Quik-Comm electronic mail public service operated by GE Information Services. District managers and dealers now communicate via Quik-Comm to exchange orders and discuss problems that formerly went directly to corporate headquarters. Electronic mail also flows between corporate and zone headquarters via the PROFs to Quik-Comm interconnection. Because everyone is now tied into the same loop, Chrysler believes that it provides dealers with faster and more accurate service, which, in turn, allows dealers to serve their customers better. The district managers, who were often left out of key communications because of telephone tag problems and who often were late submitting reports, now have a direct pipeline to corporate headquarters and dealers, which makes them more effective as well. In short, the use of electronic mail is strategic because it helps Chrysler and its dealers position themselves to improve their growing reputation for high quality service, which is critical to long-term success in the highly competitive automobile industry.

Summary

Electronic mail is a series of powerful technologies. The older ones have a long and rich history of improving communications within organizations. Telex, for example, has been around since the 1930s and has developed into a worldwide network. Because of the powerful new technologies released by microelectronic components, new electronic mail systems are developing at a far faster rate than are the older technologies. Unlike microcomputers, however, which are largely used and cost-justified by stand-alone applications, electronic mail implies group activities and must be implemented accordingly. Implementing electronic mail is a challenge both for top executives and mid-level planners. It is a challenge, however, with a real pot of gold at the end of the rainbow: *a competitive edge in the marketplace.*

Benefits and Justification

There are seven types of electronic mail technologies, which are explained in more detail in later chapters. The technologies are:

- Telex, TWX, and Mailgram;
- Facsimile;
- Communicating word processors and teletex;
- Computer-based message systems;
- Personal computers;
- Voice mail systems; and
- Computer conferencing systems.

This chapter explores the benefits and cost justification of electronic mail systems.

Direct Benefits of Electronic Mail

Electronic mail fits into a continuum of communications media, including the telephone, physical mail delivery systems, and even broadcast media such as radio and television. Each medium has its own distinct set of benefits. Electronic mail, of course, is closely associated with the telephone and physical mail systems, sharing features of both. Like the telephone, for example, electronic mail sends messages at the speed of light. Like physical mail systems, electronic mail is non-interactive: The sender does not communicate with the recipient at the same time. When the two attributes are combined, it gives electronic mail its own distinct advantages.

Electronic mail has one obvious direct benefit: It reduces the communications cycle in comparison to physical mail systems, which ranges from 1 to 2 hours for local communications to 24 hours or more for public mail systems and most couriers. Although the benefit is obvious, its impact can only be appreciated in relationship to business tasks.

To give one example, say that the company is preparing a bid for a contract and has been given 10 days to perform the task. Furthermore, assume that there are five people involved in preparing the bid from different locations. The people are from engineering, sales, marketing, and legal departments within the organization. The marketing manager has prime responsibility, but must receive approval from everyone in the other departments. Table 2-1 shows how the cycle might look using physical delivery systems, which is an example taken from the November 1, 1986 issue of *EMMS* (*Electronic Mail & Micro Systems*) newsletter published by International Resource Development, New Canaan, Conn.

Table 2-1. Document Preparation Cycle for Physical Delivery

	Step	Transmission Cost	Work Time	Elapsed Time
I.	Prepare draft 1		4 hrs.	
	Send draft	$50		1 day
	Make comments		4 hrs.	
	Return draft	$50		1 day
II.	Create draft 2		3 hrs.	
	Send draft	$50		1 day
	Make comments		2 hrs.	
	Return draft	$50		1 day
III.	Create draft 3		2 hrs.	
	Send draft	$50		1 day
	Make comments		2 hrs.	
	Return draft	$50		1 day
IV.	Prepare draft 4		1 hr.	
	Send draft	$50		1 day
	Make comments		1 hr.	
	Return draft	$50		1 day
V.	Prepare final draft		1 hr.	
	Send final draft	$50		1 day
	TOTALS	$450	20 hrs.	9 days

The example estimates the time it takes for the prime writer to create drafts, along with the time it takes for the four reviewers to make their comments. Transmission is via Federal Express at $12.50 per draft, for a total of $50 because the drafts go to four locations. As is shown, there are a total of 20 people-hours to complete the project, but an elapsed time of nine days.

Here is the same example using facsimile machines in place of Federal Express overnight courier. A facsimile machine uses an electronic scanner to capture the image of a document and transmit it at the rate of about 20 seconds per page. It is assumed that the proposal is about 10 pages long and is sent to four different locations, which takes about 30 minutes, including setup time.

Table 2-2. Document Preparation Cycle for Facsimile

	Step	Transmission Cost	Work Time	Elapsed Time
I.	Prepare draft 1		4 hrs.	
	Send draft	$15		
	Make comments		4 hrs.	
	Return draft	$15		1 day
II.	Create draft 2		3 hrs.	
	Send draft	$15		
	Make comments		2 hrs.	
	Return draft	$15		
III.	Create draft 3		2 hrs.	
	Send draft	$15		1 day
	Make comments		2 hrs.	
	Return draft	$15		
IV.	Prepare draft 4		1 hr.	
	Send draft	$15		
	Make comments		1 hr.	
	Return draft	$15		
V.	Prepare final draft		1 hr.	
	Send final draft	$15		1 day
	TOTALS	$135	20 hrs.	3 days

As can be seen, using facsimile machines allows people to turn around more than one draft of a document in a single day. This is a major benefit of all electronic mail systems. It is interesting to note, however, that although the benefit is constant, the value varies with the situation.

Value vs. Benefit

In the above example, it can be seen how electronic mail can benefit a document production task by compressing the delays associated with using couriers from a day to about a half hour. It is very possible to take a task that might take nine days and compress it to three days without having any impact on the time spent working on the document.

The value of such a benefit, however, varies with the need to perform the same amount of work in a compressed period or to allow more revisions in the same period. In the above example, say that the team works together on multiple bids. Using facsimile may allow them to put 8 to 12 revision cycles into each bid rather than 4 cycles. This might improve the quality of their bids and increase their success rate to 40 percent from 30 percent. If the average value of each bid is $30,000, for example, and the team wins $90,000 worth of contracts for every 10 bids using couriers to deliver the drafts, then the value of using facsimile versus courier is an additional $30,000 for every 10 bids. Given that the 5 facsimile (fax) machines needed for the network would cost about $20,000, then the fax machines would pay for themselves within 10 bids.

If, on the other hand, the team works full time on preparing bids and has developed an elaborate work schedule, then there is no value in reducing the transmission time alone for a single bid because it will cut into the work time on other bids, which is performed in parallel. Thus, there is no value to using facsimile unless it competes with the cost of using couriers. In the above example, however, facsimile reduced transmission costs from $450 to $135.

The above example demonstrates the two major justifications of electronic mail: value added and cost displacement. In a value-added justification, the electronic mail system improves the performance of an existing operation. If the right operation is chosen, the value can be dramatic. In a cost-displacement justification, electronic mail decreases the cost of an existing transmission system, such as a courier.

Electronic mail's benefit of decreased transmission time has both value-added and cost-displacement benefits for most organizations. The role of planners is to identify the specific applications where the benefit has value. In the bidding example above, it is hard to imagine that a company would not benefit from improving the revision cycle time in preparing bids.

There are now literally hundreds of examples of how companies are applying electronic mail's direct benefit. Most of them are related to improving the flow of time-critical information within their organizations. Thousands of financial and performance reports are now being sent using electronic mail technologies instead of by physical mail. Any company can almost assuredly improve performance by making a systematic study of the forms and reports that cause delay or add uncertainty in the decision-making process and by converting their delivery from physical to electronic mail systems.

Indirect Benefits

Electronic mail provides companies with more than just the direct benefits of improving the speed and regularity of transmitting information. There are indirect benefits that are just as important. People who use computer mailbox systems, for example, have identified a number of indirect benefits that have value to their users. Computer mailbox systems allow messages to be directed to individual mailboxes stored inside a computer. Each person on the system has a mailbox. Messages can be directed to one person or to many people. It is even possible to create distribution lists with a single name, such as the executive committee. Every person on the list receives a copy of the message. The indirect benefits of electronic mail identified are:

- Reduces telephone tag;

- Improves productivity gains of PCs and other office automation (OA) systems;

- Improves communications, especially when time zone differences make telephone communications difficult or impossible;

- Improves span of control over the activities of subordinates;

- Improves knowledge of peer activities;

- Improves group interaction and decision making; and

- Allows fewer interruptions and better time management.

Reduces Telephone Tag

Telephone tag occurs when two people keep missing each other with telephone calls. We all commonly experience telephone tag, which can continue for days. One major indirect benefit of electronic mail is that it puts a stop to telephone tag and brings efficiency to the communications cycle— as long as people check their mailboxes regularly.

Improves Productivity Gains of PCs and Other OA Systems

Personal computers and office automation systems such Digital's ALL-IN-1 have had a significant impact in most organizations by simply improving the ability of managers to create basic reports and memos. PCs and OA systems eliminate many of the shadow functions associated with creating memos and documents. The shadow functions include retyping time for secretaries and reediting time for managers. Electronic mail improves this productivity cycle even further by allowing the resulting documents and memos to be sent electronically. Because electronic mail can eliminate shadow functions associated with distribution, such as printing and copying, it can take administrative personnel out of the memo and document loop entirely, which frees their time for other tasks.

The issue of freeing time, rather than saving hard dollars, is an important one to understand. It is possible, for example, to evaluate the benefits of office automation via theoretical studies of the costs that are saved. The basic methodology is to create a scenario where managers and secretaries are saved 10 to 15 minutes per memo by using PCs and electronic mail to eliminate the shadow functions associated with manual systems. The saving is then expressed as something like $5 to $8 per memo based upon an hourly cost of employee salaries to the company.

Although the time savings may be true, the company saves no direct dollars with OA systems and electronic mail unless the head count is reduced. Thus, although it is tempting to use evaluations that express savings as several dollars per memo, in practice, this is a specious view of the real benefit of PCs, OA systems, and electronic mail. The real benefit comes from allowing employees to spend time in more productive activities.

Improves Communications Across Time Zones

For companies that are spread out geographically, electronic mail is the best means known for overcoming time zone differences, which can be significant even in the United States. Companies with employees in routine contact between California and New York only have five hours per day in which to communicate directly. If something happens at 9 A.M. on the East Coast, the manager must wait until 12 P.M. to communicate the information to the manager on the West Coast. Using a computer mailbox system or other types of electronic mail, such as facsimile, the information will be there waiting for the manager on the West Coast when the office opens.

The value of this benefit, of course, depends upon the geographical dispersion of the organization and the importance of the communication. For general communications across time zones, electronic mail allows regular communications to take place in hours rather than days, which is a tactical use of electronic mail. In time-critical situations, electronic mail can be the difference between meeting a deadline or missing it.

As an example of the importance of electronic mail across time zones, a leading computer company headquartered in the United States recently decided to become involved in a request for proposal for a major contract in Asia. The company made the decision to bid only two weeks before the due date and assigned five people to prepare the bid in the United States, where it had better document production facilities and faster access to technical personnel required to put the bid together. Management in Asia, however, had to make strategic decisions related to policy issues, which was an important part in winning the bid. The time difference was such, however, that telephone conversations could only take place after business hours in both locations.

Electronic mail was used on a daily basis by the U.S. team to discuss critical issues with management in Asia. Electronic mail was also used to send copies of the bid to management in Asia for their approval. The bid itself, which was more than 100 pages, was finished within two days of the deadline and sent electronically to Asia for a final review. Without the electronic mail system, the bid could not have been prepared in time.[1]

Improves Span of Control over the Activities of Subordinates

Al Law is a mid-level manager within Bell Canada. In 1980, he was put in charge of the marketing effort for Envoy 100, the public electronic mail service for Telecom Canada, the consortium of phone companies across Canada. He had a staff of eight people directly working on introducing Envoy 100. He also had to interact with the engineering department building the system, along with more than a dozen other people involved in its introduction, including public relations, legal, and various administrative departments. Although members of his staff had responsibility for various aspects of the introduction, such as working with the sales force, preparing the brochures, developing the pricing, etc., he had overall responsibility.

Although nobody kept track of the the numerous meetings that were involved or of the thousands of phone calls that were made, one thing was certain, Al Law could not be everywhere. Since everyone involved used the system, however, he began to notice that he had an uncanny insight into what everyone was doing. The reason was that he was being copied on communications that normally would have taken place via private phone calls or face-to-face meetings that he could not attend. Were it not for the electronic mail system, he would only find out about these communications when his staffers reported to him, if they had time. Since mailbox systems were relatively unknown back in 1980, none of the people involved realized that the span, or spreading, of knowledge concerning planning activities would be expanded; yet, it was probably the most significant benefit for Al Law, who had to be kept apprised of all of the planning activities.

When routine correspondence is transferred via a computer mailbox system, managers have better insight into the many separate communications that occur during any planning or implementation cycle. The reason is that hundreds of separate communications will take place that groups of people know about instantly, instead of having to hear of them in separate meetings, if they hear them at all. The meetings, of course, then become redundant.

The benefit has been identified in the testimony of hundreds of people who have been interviewed about their use of electronic mail. The benefit, however, has never been given a quantified value, although there have been estimates that it can shave 10 to 20 percent off the time it takes to plan and implement a project because of improved coordination. Because no company has ever set up two groups and charged them with the same planning activity, giving one a mail system and the other traditional tools, however, there can be no way to prove this benefit to the penny. Nevertheless, it is almost certainly a real benefit, according to those managers who have experienced it. Given the trend in North America to downsize middle management, improved span of control for project management may prove to be the most important benefit of electronic mail, along with its sister benefit of improving the knowledge of peer activities.

Improves Knowledge of Peer Activities

Knowing more about peer activities is closely related to an improved span of control over subordinates. Let's go back to Al Law at Bell Canada. His engineering counterpart was Burt Parsons. Although Al Law was responsible for the marketing activities, Burt Parsons was responsible for implementing the system. Each had staffs of equal size, along with responsibilities and problems of similar magnitudes. The two managers had to coordinate their activities very closely, yet had to spend most of their time on separate tasks.

By using electronic mail, each of them had far greater insight into each other's operations than would have been possible without lengthy debriefing sessions. The reason was that both parties were copied on messages that related to anything associated with joint coordination and were often included on marginally related problems. Instead of the communications flowing hierarchically, i.e., up to Al Law and across to Burt Parsons in separate steps, they often flowed from subordinates of one manager to both higher level managers simultaneously. Although each communication may have saved just minutes and provided a tiny insight into the overall planning process, when the cumulative effect of the system was considered, it amounted to many hours of saved time and a considerable improvement in insight.

Contrast this with the electronic mail company that changed CEOs in midstream, with the second CEO not using the system (see page 4). When usage of the system came to a halt, the executives no longer knew what each other was doing, except by issuing paper memos, having face-to-face meetings, or talking on the telephone. Knowledge about the activities of peers declined considerably, which increased the overhead on the group as a whole to keep their peers apprised of their activities.

The ability of peers to communicate is the cutting edge of electronic mail because it changes communication patterns within organizations. It is an obvious reason why many managers might fear using electronic mail because they perceive the system as threatening their autonomy. This is where the true nature of organizations becomes clear. Organizations that are relatively unified, with peers who work closely together for the benefit of the group, are prime candidates to derive the full benefit of electronic mail. Organizations with a lot of peer contention and departments that guard their power jealously, on the other hand, will not take full advantage of electronic mail and will tend to reject its usage, except between a peer and subordinates.

Top managers and planners must make a realistic assessment of their organizations and stress the usage patterns that are most appropriate. Preaching the benefits of improved peer coordination in the wrong organization, for example, may lead to excessive resistance.

Improves Group Interaction and Decision Making

Electronic mail helps improve group interaction and decision making. The reason is that more people can be included in making the decision because the system spans both time and distance. Consider how Beneficial Finance used its system to bring its board of directors, key executives, and key consultants together on a holiday weekend to exchange information electronically. Frank Caspersen, Beneficial's CEO, later said that the decision would have been made regardless of the system, but that the information that was available was exchanged much faster. The time frame was constant, but the level of knowledge increased for the group as a whole. Caspersen and a small coterie of executives, for example, could easily have justified making the decision themselves and presenting it to the board in a power play the next week. Although nobody can prove it, Caspersen and most others who have experienced electronic mail firmly believe that decisions improve as a result.

Like improved span of control and knowledge of peer activities, improved group interaction and the quality of decisions cannot be quantified. There is no value that a company can place on using electronic mail with the same certainty as knowing how much output will increase if specific capital investments are made to a factory.

Estimates of the value vary. Ranier Paul, Vice President of Information Services at Avon, implemented a Digital Equipment ALL-IN-1 system that integrates word processing, electronic mail, and calendars, along with self-developed data base access capability. Paul says that their studies indicate an improvement of 23 percent in the productivity of their management and professional staff. Digital itself, which operates a mail network for 65,000 employees, has performed studies in which managers indicate a productivity improvement of 5 to 15 percent because of their corporate mail system. The bottom line, however, is that the value cannot be proven to the penny. Organizations will have to take a certain risk if they want to obtain the benefits.

Fewer Interruptions and Better Time Management

The final benefit of electronic mail is one of its more controversial, yet it has been extolled time and again by users. Electronic mail replaces paper memos, telephone calls, unscheduled visits to a manager's office, and certain types of meetings. This has led to managers perceiving fewer interruptions in their daily activities and better control of their time when they use electronic mail extensively.

As an example, Wang performed a study for its voice mail system in use within a Midwestern furniture manufacturer. Users reported that interrupting phone calls dropped by 15 percent and that 75 percent of their mail messages had enough information to perform direct tasks without a clarifying return call, instead of only 25 percent of their calls before using the system.

Electronic mail's relationship to meetings and face-to-face visits should be clarified further. No medium fully replaces face-to-face contact; so, electronic mail can never be a direct replacement for meetings where important decisions must be made by a group. Electronic mail, however, can replace the need for debriefing meetings, which are held to inform a group of past and planned activities. As these meetings often take considerable time for everyone in the group to describe his or her activities, electronic mail can save considerable time over the life of a project.

Electronic mail can also serve as an excellent medium for preparing people for important meetings, which often include 80 percent background material and 20 percent discussion of critical issues. By using electronic mail during the dead time between when a meeting is called and when it is held, it is often possible to disseminate and clarify minor issues in advance of the face-to-face meeting, which can then be spent primarily on the substantive issues.

Justifying Electronic Mail

A few years back, I spoke to a VP of MIS in a leading high tech company on the West Coast. The VP boasted proudly that he would never invest in office automation unless he could justify it to the penny. I politely suggested that he was destined to never invest in OA and might end up losing his job. The reason is that most advanced information systems cannot be justified to the penny because too many variables are involved.

Consider the two types of justifications normally used to obtain hard dollar justification for a new system: value added and cost displacement. In both justifications, the inputs into the process must be known, the process itself must be measurable, and the outputs must be identifiable in order to obtain a hard dollar justification. An example of a cost-displacement situation is when the company substitutes a multiplexer for several leased telephone channels. The inputs and outputs remain constant, but the transmission cost declines. An example of a value-added justification is giving a word processor to a secretary. Although the processing cost increases, the output also increases.

In electronic mail, although there are some situations where hard dollar justification is possible, such as comparing the costs of using facsimile to using a courier service, in general, it is very difficult, if not impossible, to obtain a hard dollar justification. Consider a computer mailbox system used to improve project management via indirect benefits, such as improved ordinate-to-subordinate and peer-to-peer communications. The variables that have an impact on the communications are complex, and the process—coordinating activities and reaching decisions—is also hard to disassemble into a specific set of steps. Thus, although the mail system may be invaluable to its users, it is almost impossible to identify the precise value to the company.

Given that most companies now have electronic mail systems in operation for some of their employees, there is a natural strategy for identifying the value of the system and justifying whether it should be spread throughout the organization: *Study the perceptions and performance of existing users.* If the overwhelming majority of existing users perceive electronic mail to be valuable, chances are that they are correct. There is also likely to be hard evidence, although it may take some detective work to find it.

Here are several steps that should be included in a study of electronic mail:

- Identify specific applications where mail can be justified using a hard dollar assessment;
- Survey existing computer mailbox users, along with successful implementations at other companies;
- Assess the overall value of electronic mail;
- Create a plan to monitor ongoing performance of the electronic mail system(s); and
- Create a preliminary implementation plan.

Identify Specific Applications

Any study of electronic mail should identify specific applications that can be cost justified. These may include using facsimile to replace courier service, using voice mail to lower the cost of answering telephones within the organization, and using a computer mailbox system to transfer business forms more rapidly than using a paper delivery system.

One of the reasons for such a study is to look at the organization in a systematic way. The planners, for example, should break their organization—small or large—into its primary functional departments and study the operations of each department for potential applications. At least one person from each department, furthermore, should be included on the study team.

Survey Existing Mailbox Users

If the organization has existing electronic mail operations, they should be studied closely to understand their impact and to assess the impact of spreading these operations throughout the organization. Although most studies only consider the perception of users, it is possible to dig out corroborating facts. If, for example, users report fewer telephone calls, fewer meetings, and better management of time, it may be possible to confirm this via usage records, such as long distance telephone calls. To give one example, it may be possible to sample the records of 20 to 30 users who report a decrease in phone calls, comparing the number of their long distance calls for a few months before using electronic mail with their records after using electronic mail.

The point here is that planners should be creative in trying to corroborate the perceptions of users. It may be that no corroboration can be found because the statistics do not exist. But there is no harm in trying and a great deal of benefit. Planners should also study other case examples and may consider trading information with companies of similar size and scope in non-competitive industries.

Assess the Overall Value of Electronic Mail

When the survey and application studies are complete, they should yield a fairly clear picture of the benefits of electronic mail. Planners must then convert this into an assessment of the value to the organization. The hard dollar justifications, of course, can stand on their own. It is possible, furthermore, to put some dollar values on a computer mailbox system, although those values must be expressed in some risk relationship.

There are no rules at this point, except that the planners should be creative in converting the qualified values of electronic mail into potential hard dollar values, along with the risks of obtaining those values. When the planners do this, they create a framework in which top management can assess the upside potential versus the downside risks. This creates a reward:risk ratio that can be compared to other reward:risk ratios that compete for capital dollars. In fact, if possible, planners should build their case using the same type of evaluation format as the company uses for product-related investments. The "revenues" to be derived from electronic mail should be compared to the capital investment and to ongoing expenses of operation to provide a bottom line and an estimate of return on investment (ROI). This provides top management with the best frame of reference possible for making any long-term investment decisions.

It is suggested, however, that planners not go overboard in building a ROI evaluation. It is particularly important not to confuse the value of time savings with hard dollar savings to an organization because such an analysis is specious. As an example, unless the company plans to reduce head count because of its electronic mail or other office automation systems, it is inappropriate to suggest that electronic mail can save the company money versus manual methods of creating and distributing information, especially as the company will actually incur far more costs for the mail system than it will eliminate.

Plan for Measuring Ongoing Performance

One of the most difficult tasks is the development of a system for measuring ongoing performance of electronic mail systems. This is especially so because there are no industry-wide comparative ratio statistics available today that compare with accepted productivity ratios, such as revenues per employee. In many cases, because such statistics do not exist, no monitoring plan exists other than occasional surveys of user perceptions and some limited operational statistics, such as the time per month that each employee spends using the system.

Before expanding electronic mail, planners should identify the types of statistics that would yield valuable information about performance of the system and build their development into the ongoing costs of the system. It is particularly important to at least develop budgetary line items that clearly identify overall costs, including system operation and training. Operational statistics should also yield more than the time per month spent on the system by each user and should identify the number of messages that are sent and received by each employee, along with the length of time spent using the system and the extent of each message.

Once costs can be consolidated in a line item, it is possible to develop ratios to measure the overall impact of the system. One such ratio is a comparison of long distance telephone usage and costs to electronic mail usage and costs. Although such a ratio would have no meaning in its first year, the use of long distance telephony should decrease in comparison to electronic mail usage as a trend. In particular, people in similar positions who do not use electronic mail should have a higher average of long distance phone calls than electronic mail users.

Developing the proper statistics is both a management art and science. It is possible, for example, to spend a considerable sum and develop only useless statistics. On the other hand, investment in a proper accounting system can yield critical facts that assure management that the investment has yielded an appropriate return.

Develop an Implementation Plan

The final part of any justification to management should be a preliminary implementation plan that identifies what types of systems will be used and how they will be spread throughout the organization. For obvious reasons, planners should look toward the applications and projects that are identified as being strategic in the company's overall plans. The implementation plan is also important in obtaining support from appropriate top executives before the project is approved.

Summary

Electronic mail has numerous benefits for any organization. It is not enough, however, to throw money away on implementing the technology without a careful study of its benefits. It is also critical to obtain the approval of top management, which means being able to express the investment in familiar terms, such as a reward:risk ratio. Finally, once the investment can be justified, there must be some system to measure whether the investment has succeeded.

In short, implementing electronic mail has as much to do with proper management techniques as it does with understanding the technology. This book explores both the technology and the management technique required to implement electronic mail. Chapters 3 through 11 explore the various technologies, along with potential applications and cost justification, and chapters 12 and 13 explore the proper implementation of electronic mail.

Technology Overview

Far from being new, electronic mail has a rich history that predates the telephone. This chapter explores today's electronic mail technologies, keeping in mind that many of them have histories that date back a century or more.

19th Century Electronic Mail Technologies

The first electronic mail system went operational on May 24, 1844, when Samuel F.B. Morse's telegraph was opened between Washington, D.C., and Baltimore, Md. The first message was, "What Hath God Wrought?" To understand the importance of the telegraph, consider that its existence would have changed the course of many a war and, had it been available in 1812, might have changed the history of the United States. Two weeks before the famous Battle of New Orleans was fought, U.S. and British negotiators in England reached a stand-in-place treaty in which the British were allowed to consolidate their forces in the Gulf of Mexico. The message of that treaty, however, took 30 days to reach Washington, D.C., from London. Had the telegraph been in existence, the Battle of New Orleans, which resulted in the British being pushed from North America, might not have been fought.

Had the British remained to consolidate their forces, they might have prevented the fledgling United States from its Western expansion. Had the telegraph been in existence in 1812, North America might now consist of a number of separate countries.[1]

Telegraphy to Telex

The telegraph has served as the father of telex, which is the best known electronic mail technology in existence today. The telegraph was based on a three-digit code developed by Morse. Although few people actually know the code today, most people know its name.

Telex is based on a five-digit code called Baudot, which is named after a French postal engineer who worked on telegraphy in the 1870s. Like the Morse code, the Baudot code was adopted as a standard by the International Telegraph Union, which was formed in 1865 to regulate the development and standardization of telegraph systems worldwide.[2]

The Baudot code was intended for electronic versions of the typewriter that were just starting to become popular in businesses. Unfortunately, the cost of producing such devices was prohibitive, which left the code only one use—in manual systems. The Baudot code, however, was too complex to replace the three-digit Morse code. So its use languished until the 1930s when the Teletype Corporation introduced the first low cost electronic communicating typewriters. From there, usage began spreading in private wire telecommunication systems, as well as in a new public service called the Teletypewriter Exchange (Telex), which was first introduced in Germany in 1935. In the past 50 years, telex has become worldwide in scope incorporating more than 2 million terminals. Although it is outdated technologically—with a transmission rate of six characters per second (cps) and a transmission network that does not check for errors—telex usage is still growing at a rate of about 8 percent per year. According to the Federal Communications Commission's (FCC) "Statistics of Regulated Common Carriers, 1985", regulated telex carriers handled about $650 million worth of telex messages sent within, to, and from the United States.

Telex embodies the similarity between electronic mail and the telephone because the switching systems are identical. In fact, older telex machines have rotary dials with the same mechanisms used in rotary-dial telephones. The user dials another telex machine number, waits for an answerback (a signal of up to 23 characters that is sent out by the receiving telex machine that confirms its identity to the sender), and then transmits the message. What gets typed on the sender's terminal is reproduced on the receiver's machine in real-time. In effect, the only differences between telex and the telephone is that the messages are textual, not verbal, and that they are stored. Initial telex machines used paper for storage; modern machines use magnetic disk, magnetic tape, or paper.

Facsimile—Sending Images Electronically

Although telegraphy was the first electronic mail technology, facsimile—the supposedly modern technology that allows sending images electronically—is almost as old. Facsimile was invented in 1842 by Scottish clockmaker Alexander Bain who was working on the problem of how to synchronize his myriad clocks electronically so that they would all keep the same time. In the process, Bain discovered that if he moved raised metallic letters from top to bottom across a moving pendulum carrying a current, when the pendulum brushed across the tips of the letters, it would send a current; when it was in the open air, however, no current was sent. To duplicate the image of the letters, Bain used a paper coated with a chemical that would change colors when it received an electric charge. Bain received British patent 9745 in 1843 in recognition of his invention.[3]

The first operational facsimile system was established in France in 1865 by an Italian, Giovanni Caselli, who succeeded in linking Paris with several other French cities. Caselli's system never caught on, however, and facsimile languished. The reason for this was that the technology did not exist to scan documents properly, although the technologies existed to transmit them and print their images. In 1902, German inventor Dr. Arthur Korn publicly demonstrated the first effective solution to facsimile's problem by developing a photo-electric scanning system. In 1910, the system was employed to send pictures between London, Berlin, and Paris. In 1922, it was used to send a picture of Pope Pius XI from Rome to the United States; it was published on the same day by the *New York World*.[4]

Although facsimile found its niche in specialized applications, such as sending photographs, weather maps, and fingerprints, it didn't become a mainstream business technology until the late 1960s when Western Union and Xerox introduced relatively low cost facsimile machines designed for the general business user. These machines were electronic mail devices in the truest sense of the term. The Xerox machine became the most popular and garnered a base of almost 100,000 units, along with an 80-percent share of the market by the mid-1970s because of high-powered marketing techniques. The machine that Xerox used, interestingly, was a modern implementation of a device first designed in the 1850s by British inventor Frederick Bakewell. It used what is called the screw-and-cylinder technique in which the paper is wrapped around a drum and the scanning and printing devices are moved down the paper using a screw-thread mechanism. Although the machine was slow—sending a page in six minutes—it was a lot faster than using the mail.

The Xerox unit, however, had more than slowness going against it. It used what was known as burn-off paper, which was made with a thin layer of carbon sandwiched between regular paper and a chemical coating that oxidized when it received an electronic impulse, showing the carbon underneath. The chemicals, however, gave off fumes that often left operators with headaches, which is one of the major reasons why facsimile was not popular for use in general offices. In addition, the reproduction was not particularly good because of the resolution of the burn-off paper and the scanner, which was 96 lines per inch. Finally, although the machines were not expensive— renting for under $100 per month— communication costs at six minutes per page were quite high.

Despite the negatives of Xerox's facsimile machine, it created a new industry and attracted a number of major competitors, such as 3M and a well funded startup, Graphic Sciences, which raised almost $30 million in 1968 to invest in facsimile. Graphic Sciences was later sold to Burroughs in the mid-1970s and to Fujitsu in 1986. Throughout the late 1960s and 1970s, these firms fought fiercely to establish facsimile as a mainstream business technology and are still amongst the leading suppliers in the industry today.

Modern Electronic Mail Technologies

Although electronic mail may not be new, it has certainly waited for low cost technologies to make its direct use popular. Most businesses, for example, have facsimile and telex machines in communication centers within their office buildings. The typical business user, however, rarely even sees these machines, let alone touches them directly. This has an enormous impact on usage when one considers that habit is probably the major barrier to usage. If it is out of sight, it is often out of mind. Thus, although major businesses have had both telex and facsimile machines for years, usage has been relatively low, not only because of the cost and quality, but also because many users do not think of using the technologies when they have the need.

Today, there are seven basic categories of electronic mail systems on the market. Without exception, they are all a far cry from the electronic mail systems of even the 1970s. The categories are:

- Telex, TWX, and Mailgram;
- Facsimile;
- Communicating word processors and teletex;
- Computer-based message systems;
- Personal computers;
- Voice mail systems; and
- Computer conferencing systems.

Telex, TWX, and Mailgram

Although the basic telex system remains the same in terms of speed, telex terminals have come a long way. Old telex machines still abound, but the majority have been replaced by terminals with built-in electronic editors; improved storage mechanisms, such as floppy or hard disks; and other features, such as a CRT monitor for message preparation. Telex has also spread so steadily that it is the world's largest integrated electronic mail network with about 2 million users listed in public directories. Revenues generated from telex are a few billion dollars worldwide, even though telex is still a slow means of communication— transmitting at only 6 cps, in comparison to the average personal computer, which transmits at 120 cps.

In North America, telex is used primarily for international communications, not as a tool for domestic communications. Telex executives, for example, have estimated that 60 to 80 percent of the telexes generated on terminals in North America are sent overseas. This is particularly true in the United States, which has a total of only 140,000 telex terminals. Western Union has the largest network, with 75,000 telex installations. ITT Worldcom, RCA Globecom, and MCI International also have significant networks, with a combined total of 65,000 terminals. In Canada, there are 40,000 telex terminals operated by CNCP Telecommunications. Telex, incidentally, is far more popular in Canada than in the United States. Although the ratio of U.S. to Canadian population is about 10:1, the ratio of telex machines is only 2.5:1.

In the mid-1950s, AT&T introduced a competitive service to telex called TWX, which uses the 8 digit ASCII code instead of Baudot. TWX also has a slightly faster transmission speed of 10 cps. Today, the TWX network, which has been renamed Telex II, is operated by Western Union in the United States (it was purchased from AT&T) and by Telecom Canada in Canada. There are about 75,000 TWX machines in the United States, which are used primarily for domestic communications, and only 5,000 TWX terminals in Canada, most of which are used primarily for communication within the telephone industry itself. Western Union, furthermore, has integrated TWX with its telex network via store-and-forward message switching so that users on one network can send messages to users on the other network. Telex and TWX networks are also integrated with numerous computer-based message systems (CBMS) so that the 250,000-plus telex and TWX terminals in North America can be accessed by the more than 1 million users on CBMS.

Western Union, incidentally, has contributed many advances to electronic mail, including the term itself. Although no one knows when the term "electronic" mail was first used, Western Union started using it in the late 1960s to describe a service it was setting up to connect its telex and TWX terminals to approximately 140 United

States Postal Service (USPS) offices across the United States. These locations were strategically chosen because they allowed messages to be printed out and delivered as letters the next day anywhere in the United States.

The service, called Mailgram, was announced in 1972, and proved to be so successful that Western Union quickly expanded its use to the general public via operators who would enter Mailgrams from people who phoned in and to large bulk mailers, who provided Western Union with multiple messages on magnetic tapes that were run on a special computer connected to the Mailgram network. Mailgram has also become the model for a number of electronic mail services that interconnect terminals with paper delivery systems, such as the USPS mail system and same-day or overnight courier services. In 1974, Western Union registered the term "electronic mail" as a trademark. Western Union, however, has never defended the trademark, and electronic mail today is a generic term open for use by anybody.

Facsimile

Facsimile has come a long way since the days of Xerox's burn-off machine that sent a page in six minutes. Because of their non-alphabetic character set, the Japanese invested heavily in facsimile as a technology in the mid-1970s, pushing the state of the art into a new era in a short 10 years. A number of leading Japanese facsimile manufacturers, for example, succeeded in having the CCITT, which is the International Telecommunications Union's standards-making arm, create international facsimile standards for their new technology so that machines from different vendors could communicate. In the early days of business facsimile— in the 1960s and 1970s— machines from Xerox, 3M, and Burroughs would not intercommunicate.

Today's modern facsimile machine looks and operates almost like a small office copier. Pages are read electronically in seconds by fiber optic-based scanners with only one moving part— the mechanism that pushes the paper past the scanner. Using digital compression techniques, the image of a printed page is reduced in size and transmitted in under 20 seconds at a speed of 9,600 bits per second (bps) over the regular telephone network using step-down modems. If the machines cannot communicate at 9,600 bps because of line problems, they automatically readjust to transmission at 4,800 bps or slower until the page can be transmitted accurately.

Printing is also done on a solid-state mechanism with only two moving parts: one moves the paper past the printing mechanism, and the other cuts the paper off when the page is finished. The paper is thermal paper, which is widely used in small calculators. Thermal paper has a thin coated layer that changes color when heat is applied. The facsimile machine's print head consists of tiny electrodes spread across the page. Each electrode heats up and cools rapidly, allowing a complete line to be printed at a time.

The final advance has been in price. A basic version of the facsimile machine described above is priced as low as $1,500 with a 4,800 bps modem, although feature-rich units with 9,600 bps transmission, logging capabilities, automatic dialers, interfaces to disk-based store-and-forward mechanisms, and the ability to receive and print from ASCII terminals are closer to the $4,000 range. In contrast, Xerox's six-minute per page unit introduced in 1968 was priced at about $2,500.

As might be expected, the technological advances in facsimile have opened up the industry dramatically. Facsimile has moved out of communication centers into the mainstream as an office communication device. Facsimile cards, for example, have been developed for personal computers, minicomputers, and mainframes so that facsimile machines can communicate to these computers directly. For about $1,000, it is possible to turn an IBM PC into a self-standing facsimile machine, although the user requires a separate scanning system to input paper documents. The CCITT is easing this process considerably through its international standards that now specify the integration of facsimile and computing.

Facsimile is now one of the most popular electronic mail devices in use today. Since 1982, according to export statistics from the Japanese Ministry of Trade and Industry (MITI), 2.3 million digital facsimile machines were exported by Japanese companies worldwide.[5]

Communicating Word Processors and Teletex

When word processors were in their heyday in the late 1970s and early 1980s, it seemed natural to have documents transmitted from one machine to another electronically. The word processors had all the tools required other than modems and add-on communications cards. In response to the seeming demand, all word processing manufacturers added communications to their capabilities. The demand reached such a crescendo that most users would not buy a machine unless it was capable of having communications added as an option.

Surprisingly, although users demanded the option of adding communications, few actually implemented the feature. So-called communicating word processors (CWPs) are a technological reality, but they have been largely a market bust, with less than 5 percent of the installed base of word processors ever adding communications.

Though the reasons have never been qualified, it is normally attributed to the lack of standardization amongst file formats of the different word processing brands on the market and to the cost of the communications options, which is about $2,000.

It is likely, however, that far more was involved—particularly the document preparation environment. Certain document-intensive parts of corporations, such as legal departments, adopted communications quickly and still use CWPs. Document preparation by the typical manager, however, has never fit the same mold. In legal departments, documents are typically sent to a small number of individuals in well defined locations, allowing a complete application to be developed where the document is prepared at one location and sent to another location for editing and final printing.

The typical manager, however, has a varying list of potential document recipients scattered throughout an organization. In addition, graphics or other visual material are often added to the documents. Although the one or two graphs or charts may total less than 5 percent of the total document content, any document with a chart or graph is not suitable to be communicated. In short, the CWP concept never fit the reality of how business documents are assembled and communicated. Although the CWP may make sense when one copy of a document is being sent to a specific department, its effectiveness is limited when seven copies must be sent to four different locations, which is a more typical pattern for most business documents. In this environment, it is not the place where the document is prepared that is important, but rather the place where the document is copied and distributed.[6] This, far more than cost or compatibility, has been why CWPs largely have failed.

As testimony to the lack of popularity of CWPs, the CCITT developed a standard for CWPs called teletex,[7] which has been finalized for more than five years. Teletex was developed to kill two birds with one stone. First, it was expected to replace the telex network with devices that send at 240 cps. Second, it was expected to solve the word processor standardization problem by dictating a file format that all vendors had to follow. Since the standard has been approved, vendors of word processors have been pressured by telecommunication authorities in Europe to introduce teletex versions that work with their word processors. Virtually every CWP vendor has complied; thus, numerous machines are now available on the market.

Nevertheless, at this writing, there are less than 20,000 teletex machines installed worldwide—according to electronic mail consultants familiar with the teletex world—and only a few hundred in North America, despite optimistic predictions by proponents that the installed base would reach above 100,000 by the end of the decade. There is also no evidence that teletex is building up momentum to make a major push into user organizations. The reason is almost certainly that the CWP does not meet real needs when it functions as a separate terminal as does the telex machine. Something more is required to turn electronic document transmission into a reality.

Computer-Based Message Systems

The computer has opened up the door to the modern era of electronic mail. Although this may be a truism understood by anyone in the office world, the specifics of how the computer has impacted electronic mail and how its impact will evolve has already left considerable confusion. Computers were first used to send electronic mail in the early 1960s when message switching systems were developed. The switching systems worked with defined terminals connected to the computer. Messages were sent from one terminal, stored for a short period of time, and then delivered to the recipient terminal(s). These systems were developed as improvements over telex and TWX, however, not as systems to be used directly by millions of individual users. The primary reason was cost. Early message switching systems were very expensive, costing a few million dollars or more. Terminals were also expensive, costing about $3,000 each. These message switching systems were put in place by governmental agencies, the military, and large businesses, such as airlines and banks, who could afford their high cost. Western Union also added a store-and-forward message switch called Infocom that provided specialized services to both its telex and TWX users.

Today's CBMS, interestingly, did not evolve from the early message switching systems. Instead, today's CBMS evolved from the work of academic and military researchers, including the small telecommunications engineering firm of Bolt, Baranek & Newman (BBN), on a special packet switching network called the ARPANET, which was set up by the U.S. military's Defense Advanced Research Projects Agency (DARPA) in 1968 to handle communications between computer terminals and host computers. These researchers were like any other group of people who had trouble reaching each other by telephone— with one exception: They all had computer terminals connected to a myriad of host computers on the most advanced computer communications network in the world.

In 1970, Dr. Lawrence Roberts, the Director of the Information Processing Techniques Office at DARPA, wrote two programs, RDMAIL and SNDMSG, that simulated a post office mailbox system. Users had their own mailboxes on the computer that ran RDMAIL and SNDMSG so that they could sign on, read their incoming mail, and then send messages to other people's mailboxes for later retrieval.

In 1972, programmers from BBN wrote a more comprehensive mail system for ARPANET users that added features such as the ability to reply to the message being read, forward the message to other recipients, or file the message for later retrieval. BBN's program, called Hermes, is often considered to be the first popular CBMS. Although one can look at the concept of the mailbox as the major technological innovation of the CBMS versus traditional message switching systems, the real power underlying the CBMS is its ability to be used directly by people within an organization. Each person has an identity within the CBMS rather than each having a terminal. This personal nature of the CBMS impacts the daily activities of its users far more than does any other electronic mail system and allows the CBMS to be used as a substitute for making telephone calls and for sending office memos to a higher degree than does any other electronic mail system.

Although it took a few years for the CBMS to permeate the general business community, its adoption has been almost instantaneous when compared to the 19th Century technologies— telegraphy and facsimile— or to telex. In less than 14 years, public CBMS services have been introduced on the commercial market by virtually every major communications company and by a number of timesharing firms. Many large companies have also developed their own CBMS software or purchased software for in-house services. The CBMS, furthermore, has become synonymous with the term electronic mail. The features available to CBMS users also have expanded considerably. Today, most CBMS services offer users the ability to program electronic business forms and also to interconnect with other electronic mail networks such as telex, TWX, and Mailgram. In addition, most services allow users to send electronic mail letters for delivery by courier services or by the postal system.

Nevertheless, CBMS services are still only a small part of the electronic mail industry in terms of revenues, although they have the largest number of users by far. According to the EMA, there are close to 5 million CBMS users in North America, with about 1 million users on public services and 3.7 million on in-house systems. Many of the most important developments in the field, for example, have taken place within large companies such as Hewlett-Packard, Digital Equipment Corp., IBM, Texas Instruments, Procter & Gamble, and other large corporations, which all operate extensive electronic mail networks.

Although the CBMS today is probably behind telex and facsimile in the electronic mail industry—based upon the amount of money paid for usage and hardware—it is the most important development in the industry and is the key to the future of electronic mail. The reason for this is that the CBMS does not have to function alone in competition with facsimile, telex, and other electronic mail technologies but can become the network hub around which all types of electronic mail systems operate. As an example, most modern CBMS are interconnected with the telex network, enabling users to send and receive messages with telex subscribers. Thus, the integration of different technologies is already underway and will develop at an accelerated pace in the late 1980s and early 1990s.

Personal Computers

The PC has already played an important role in electronic mail by its very existence. In the early 1980s, one of the major roadblocks to implementing CBMS was the lack of terminals inside user organizations. Although the rate charged for using CBMS services has been less costly than the rate for long distance telephony since the late 1970s, the cost of installing terminals has retarded implementation considerably. In 1980, for example, a low cost terminal and modem were priced at about $1,300, which added up to a sizeable expense for a group with 50 to 100 users, few of whom would normally have a communicating device on their desks. Furthermore, it has always been difficult to justify installing a terminal solely to use electronic mail, especially because of the valuable real estate that the terminal takes up on users' desks.

The PC has largely solved the barrier of available terminals. More than 9 million PCs are now installed in businesses throughout North America, with the number growing monthly. These PCs were largely purchased for applications other than electronic mail, such as word processing, financial analysis (spreadsheets), and data base handling. Thus, the ability to send electronic mail represents an incremental cost to the initial investment in the PC, which makes it far easier to justify. Most PCs can add the ability to access electronic mail systems for a cost below $200 for a 1,200 bps modem and as low as $295 for a 2,400 bps modem. A more typical cost for a 1,200 bps modem with software, however, is in the $300 to $400 range. In effect, the cost of adding electronic mail for most users has dropped 200 percent in just five years. The impact is already being felt by the electronic mail community, with a very high percentage of its users operating with personal computers.

Although the PC has already played a major role in electronic mail, this does not mean that electronic mail systems have been well integrated with PCs. In many cases, CBMS are set up to operate with simple, line-oriented ASCII files that have carriage returns after 80-character lines and no special format codes. PCs, on the other hand, are most effective at running word processing, data base, or spreadsheet programs that require specially formatted files. In a word processor, for example, a carriage return is placed at the end of each paragraph, not at the end of each line. The file itself, furthermore, has special codes embedded and cannot be read directly by the CBMS.

Although most word processors have utilities that translate their formatted files into ASCII files with carriage returns every line, this has typically required users to run three separate programs (the word processor, the file translation program, and the telecommunications program) to transmit a file to an electronic mail system. Also, CBMS typically do not have an end-to-end error detection-correction protocol when receiving files, which means that the user must reread the file after it has been transmitted in order to make certain that it was received without errors. In short, although using an electronic mail system to perform a task such as sending an overnight letter seems to be an easy, cost-effective way to do business, the shadow functions associated with communicating from a PC to an electronic mail service often make it more cost-effective to print the letter out locally and hand it to Federal Express or another courier service for next day delivery.

The relationship between the PC and the CBMS, however, is just beginning. Already, sophisticated software is on the market that makes it far easier to connect into CBMS. The CBMS vendors are also adding special features that make them more suitable for interaction with PCs. But the relationship is still in its early days. Advances are already in the implementation stages, however, that will make the interaction of PCs and CBMS almost seamless during the next few years. In fact, in many cases, the user will not know whether the CBMS is controlling the PC, or vice versa.

It is important to think of PCs in relationship to CBMS; yet, PCs can also function as independent electronic mail devices in their own right. This has been greatly aided by telecommunications software for PCs, which normally has an error-free file transfer mode. Numerous users have already set up small networks of PCs for the purpose of transferring formatted files and computer programs. One PC vendor, Epson America, once had its programming team scattered throughout the United States because of the ability to ship programs amongst them error-free. There are also thousands of PC-based bulletin board systems operating in North America, with formatted file transfers a major application. Telenet, which has a nationwide packet switching network, has even set up a special service called PC Pursuit that is designed to allow users to transfer files to major cities in the United States during evening hours at a flat rate of $25 per month with unlimited usage. The purpose of the service is to allow PC users to avoid long distance telephone costs when calling bulletin boards in different cities.

Despite the almost natural tendency for PCs to function as electronic mail devices, most PCs still largely function as stand-alone devices within their offices. Most estimates indicate that no more than 25 to 40 percent of business PCs that are sold have modems, which would put the modem population for PCs in the 3 to 4 million range. It is this base of users that has made electronic mail an exciting new industry, fueling life into the CBMS and data base access industries, despite a number of serious obstacles to easy usage. As PCs increase in power and as communications software increases in sophistication, usage levels will rise dramatically.

Voice Mail Systems

Voice mail systems have existed since the late 1950s, when the first answering machines were developed. Today, answering machines are commonplace and are purchased by millions of people yearly. Technically, answering machines are electronic mail devices, although they are not going to be covered in this book because of their simplicity. The book does cover those voice mail systems, however, that are CBMS that are programmed to handle voice rather than text.

Voice mail was pioneered by two companies: IBM and VMX. IBM did research in the early 1970s into voice mail and produced the Audio Distribution System (ADS), which was based on the Series 1 minicomputer. VMX, which holds the major patents on voice mail, developed its system during the same period and is now the leading vendor in the market. There is nothing fancy about voice mail systems. They work just like text-based CBMS. Users have IDs and can access electronic mailboxes that house their messages. While on the system, users can read, send, reply to, and forward their voice mail, although they cannot file messages in personal files because of high storage costs. Unlike text mail systems, however, which require ASCII terminals or PCs, voice mail systems are controlled by the touch-tone pads on telephones or by tone generator pads on rotary dial phones. This opens up a base of more than 200 million telephones in North America that can be used to operate voice mail systems.

Voice mail systems may operate like text-based CBMS, but there the similarities end. Text-based CBMS have thrived as nationwide public services because of their low cost of access via packet switching networks, which are covered in the following chapter. Voice mail systems have done poorly as nationwide services because of the high cost of long distance telephony. Instead, voice mail systems are best suited when the access is local— either within a city or on a Private Branch Exchange (PBX) inside an office building. Today, every major digital PBX on the market has at least one, and sometimes two or three, voice mail systems that are integrated to such a degree that the system functions like a CBMS and a telephone answering machine. When a user leaves the office, calls are forwarded to the voice mail system, which answers with the user's own voice, explaining that he or she is unavailable to take the calls. This has led a number of companies to sell voice mail on the grounds that it lowers telephone handling costs within a company.

The connection with PBXs has given voice mail a very different purchasing pattern than text-based CBMS, which are normally purchased either as timesharing services from outside vendors or as software packages that are to be run on existing in-house mainframes or minicomputers. Voice mail systems are sold or leased with both the hardware and software by PBX vendors or by independent telecommunication suppliers. From an accounting viewpoint, text-based CBMS are normally viewed as a corporate expense, whereas voice mail systems are viewed as a capital purchase or lease. There is also a more subtle point here that has implications for electronic mail. Voice mail, because it has evolved as a PBX add-on, usually comes under the purview of the manager of telecommunications within most organizations. Text-based CBMS, however, are usually placed under the manager of data processing, primarily by default. Telex and facsimile, furthermore, have traditionally been grouped under the manager of office administration, whereas communicating word processors have been purchased by the manager of the word processing department. In effect, modern electronic mail has developed in such a way that few companies, if any, have one person or group with the full authority to champion its overall evolution within an organization. This, as much as any other factor, has slowed the development of electronic mail in North America.

To date, voice mail has been a disappointment in the market. Analysts once predicted that voice mail alone would grow rapidly into a multi-billion dollar market, with a high percentage of the PBXs in North America adding voice mail as a standard feature for users. The capital cost of voice mail systems, however, has proven to be a barrier.

Even though text-based terminals or PCs are not involved, voice mail systems still cost from $100 to $300 per user. A PBX with 300 users' extensions, for example, requires a voice mail system priced in the $60,000 to $90,000 range. As a result, most companies have held back on major purchases, with the result that there are only a few thousand voice mail systems in operation today, although there are more than 150,000 PBXs that are capable of adding voice mail.

There is also the interesting potential to have voice mail integrated with central office telephone switches and offered to the public by local telephone companies. To date, Telecom Canada has held a limited trial of voice mail; but no such trials have been held in the United States, where it has met with strong industry resistance because of competitive issues. Even if the phone companies are permitted to offer voice mail services, however, it is questionable whether such services will be able to compete with the simplest electronic mail device— the home answering machine.

Computer Conferencing

When text-based CBMS were first developed, a number of researchers began working on a version that was designed to handle group meetings rather than just individual messages. These systems, called computer conferencing, still have a sender, receiver, message, and feedback, except the file structure is very different. A text-based CBMS is set up so that each person has a mailbox, with messages addressed specifically to him or her.

In a computer conferencing system, the sender addresses messages to specific conferences (or meetings) instead of to a specific person. The conferences are attended by specific people on the system. Public conferences are open to everyone, whereas private conferences are open to a collection of specific people. Attendees can sign on at their own convenience, read the comments sent by other attendees, and make their own responses. In the process, a written record of the conference is created, which is the equivalent of having a stenographer take down the record of a meeting. In fact, the relationship between text-based CBMS and computer conferencing systems is identical to the relationship between making telephone calls or writing memos and attending meetings, which leads to an interesting phenomenon.

Although text-based CBMS have found relatively rapid acceptance by users, computer conferencing has caught on very slowly in the business world. Nevertheless, people typically spend far more time in meetings than they do on the telephone and writing memos combined.[8] In theory, using a computer conferencing system should be far more productive to an organization than using a text-based CBMS. In practice, users have opted for the opposite. Something other than logic is clearly involved. To give an idea of the level of usage of computer conferencing, there are probably less than 100 systems installed privately in businesses within North America and perhaps 5 public computer conferencing services designed for serious business use. Usage is at least an order of magnitude less than on message-oriented CBMS services.

Computer conferencing has caught on in only two areas: the academic environment and with PC buffs. Numerous universities have computer conferencing systems in operation, with trials performed yearly with both government and business users. PC buffs have also adopted the electronic bulletin board as a phenomenon. In cities nationwide, a few thousand bulletin board systems operating rudimentary conferencing systems have popped up, with more being added weekly.

Summary

There are now seven different types of electronic mail systems operating in North America. Although these systems have all developed separately, strong forces are now underway to integrate these technologies into one overall system via both custom interconnections and the X.400 Message Handling Standard developed by the CCITT. Certain integrations are already well underway, such as the connection between CBMS and telex, TWX and Mailgram, and the connection between CBMS and computer conferencing systems. Other integrations, such as a combined voice and text mail system, have been introduced by a few advanced vendors. Still other integrations, such as the connection of facsimile into telex, teletex, and CBMS, are now in the design stage and early implementation.

Although most of this book will be devoted to the separate technologies, as well as to implementation strategies, readers should keep in mind that the real power of electronic mail will not be unleashed until these technologies are integrated and corporatewide networks evolve. The X.400 Standard will play a critical role because it will not only allow different CBMS to intercommunicate, but will also allow interconnection with telex, teletex, facsimile, and voice mail networks. Such full integration, however, is likely to exist by the early to mid-1990s.

Communication Roadways

One of the major events in the modern history of North America was the development of the automobile industry. From the dream of early entrepreneurs to build horseless carriages for the wealthy few who could afford them, the auto industry evolved over a few decades into a mass production industry that cranked out cars for the growing middle class.

In the development of the automobile, there is a lesson of great importance for electronic mail. The automobile alone was not enough to build an industry. Of equal importance was the development of the roadway system, which gave drivers mobility. In fact, it was the system of roads in North America, especially the wide freeways and superhighways that were developed in the United States with funding from the *Interstate Highway Act* of 1956, that ultimately determined the types of cars that were produced. Furthermore, after the roadway system was completed in the 1960s, builders discovered a great opportunity— the suburban shopping center.

The same analogy holds for electronic mail— or for any other remote information or data processing service. Terminals, communication networks, and host computers are connected in a symbiotic relationship: Each defines the limitations of the others. The existence of terminals will determine the willingness to invest in communication networks to tap their potential. When the networks are built, it will prompt users to put up hosts with applications to take advantage of the terminals. In this way, terminals are like cars, with the information they generate being sent on communication roadways to host computers that function like retail stores. This chapter explores the communication roadways in existence today, along with their relationship to electronic mail terminals and hosts.

Communication Roadways and E-Mail

Electronic mail is limited by the roadways over which the mail can travel. Although this is so obvious it seems trivial, its implications are so profound that they must be explored. The roadways, quite literally, limit the hardware, software, user interfaces, and applications for electronic mail and have even played a major role in determining the suppliers of public CBMS services. It is no accident, for example, that the major CBMS service suppliers are telecommunication or time-sharing companies who have invested in underlying networks.[1] The CBMS were developed to help generate traffic on their networks.

A more subtle impact has been on how users have been limited in their ability to interact with electronic mail systems. The slow speed of today's networks, whose local access loops operate at 300, 1,200, or 2,400 bps with most terminals, make it impossible to operate sophisticated, full-screen editors on the host with any kind of user-friendliness. Such editors require screen refresh rates of at least 9,600 bps in order to function smoothly. This has restricted CBMS to line-oriented editors, which are difficult to learn and cumbersome to use in comparison to the word processors available on PCs. Although PCs open the door to offline editing and file transfer, this is still a slow process that requires users to wait while files are shipped at slow speeds from the host to the PC, or vice versa.

There is also a revolution going on in communication roadways, that is disrupting electronic mail planning just as building new roadways disrupts automobile travel. In effect, planning for electronic mail systems has extra confusion because the roadways themselves are in a period of confusion and change. In fact, the situation in communications networks is far more complex than it ever was on automobile travel because communication roadways have seven different levels of functionality that are all in flux at the same time.

In today's world, there are five types of roadways that are used for electronic mail: telex, telephone, packet switching, wide area networks, and local area networks (LANs). Telex, telephone, packet switching, and wide area networks are typically operated by public telecommunication carriers and by private companies for use inside their companies. LANs are typically operated privately within individual organizations.

The Telephone Network

The telephone can be described as a user-friendly network. The caller punches a few numbers on a simple keyboard and almost like magic is connected to another person. The network has become so sophisticated that it is now possible to reach people driving their cars in different countries around the globe. Behind the telephone on a desk, however, is an extremely sophisticated, and rapidly changing, network. Telephone companies worldwide are now struggling with the task of updating their networks to match the sophistication of present-day terminals, PCs, and hosts.

Basic Elements of the Network

The telephone network itself consists of two primary elements: switches and communication channels. In North America, telephones can be reached by a 10-digit number, e.g., 313-994-4030, with the prefix 1 used to signal that the call is long distance. The number represents the area code, the local exchange, and the specific telephone. Each telephone is given a 4-digit number, which identifies it within the local exchange where the telephone is connected. The local exchanges, in turn, are given 3-digit numbers. Local exchanges are grouped in Local Access Transport Areas (LATAs), which are identified by the "area code". In all, there are 161 LATAs in the United States, thousands of local exchanges, and millions of individual telephones.

The Switches

Telephone switches are organized on regional (Class 1), sectional (Class 2), and primary (Class 3) levels. Each switch, furthermore, is connected to a toll center switch (Class 4) that collects information on the calls. Class 1, 2, and 3 switches are used to route calls throughout the network. The final step in the switching process is the local exchange, also called the end central office (Class 5), which is connected to each telephone throughout the network.[2] Calls originate at the end central offices and are routed through primary, sectional, and regional switches as required. The calls are sent via trunk lines that connect the switching network together. Three more types of switches are important. The first is the tandem switch, which is used to connect different end central offices or long distance switches located within an area. The second is the Private Branch Exchange (PBX), which is used by private organizations to switch telephone calls within a building or campus. The third is Class 4 toll switches that handle billing and administration. Figure 4-1 shows a diagram of how the telephone system is organized.

The telephone network has gone through what amounts to culture shock over the past 10 years. For most of the history of the telephone, switching was done with electromechanical systems that simulated how a manual operator would place a telephone call. Since the mid-1970s, however, electronic switches have moved into the telephone network. These electronic switches at first used digital processors to control electromechanical switching elements. Today, new switches are completely digital so that information moves through them as bits of digital information rather than as analog wave signals. These new switches open up numerous new methods of defining networks and routing calls via software control, rather than via electromechanical switching.

Figure 4-1. Diagram of the Public Telephone Network

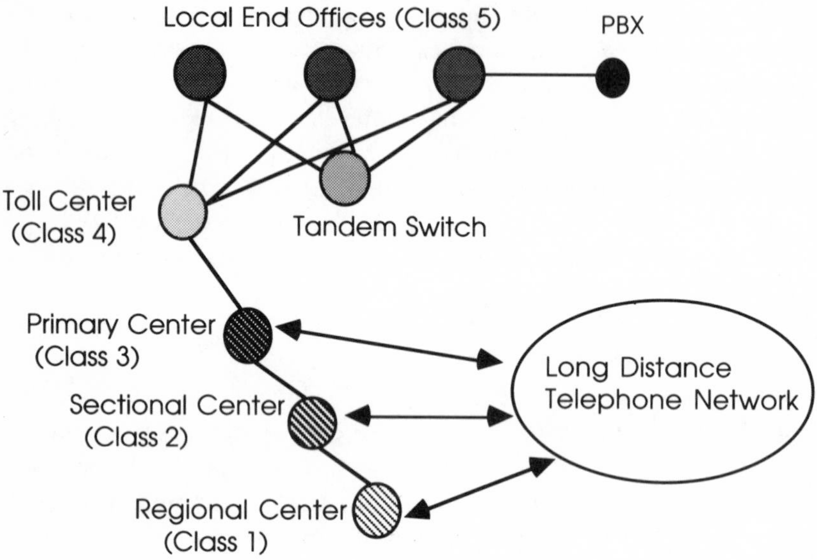

Telephone Communication Channels

Telephone calls can be sent over two media: cables and the air. Cables can be made of twisted pair wire, coaxial cables, or fiber-optic cable; communication via air is handled by microwave or satellite radio systems. Local telephones are all connected via twisted pair cables to end central offices. Switching systems within cities are also typically connected via cables, although it is also possible to have microwave communication links as well. Long distance telephony, however, is a mixture of microwave or satellite radio, twisted pairs, coaxial cables, and fiber-optic cables. Microwave and satellite long distance systems were the most popular in the 1960s, 1970s, and early 1980s; fiber-optic cables are becoming more popular today and will likely become the major means of sending telephone signals in the 1990s and beyond.

The signal itself can be sent via analog or digital means. Central telephone offices and their local phones are still connected via analog signalling techniques, which means that signals are wave patterns that vary based on the parameters of the voice signal. When a call leaves an end central office, however, it does not always travel as an analog signal throughout the network. Until the 1960s, all calls were sent using Frequency Division Multiplexing (FDM), which breaks up a wideband channel into multiple analog frequency bands. A coaxial cable, for example, can be broken up to handle 600 simultaneous calls using FDM techniques. In the 1960s, digital techniques began to be used. Calls were converted from analog signals into digital pulses using Time Division Multiplexing (TDM) techniques in which the bits from many different calls are inserted into time slots at a high rate of speed. Today, the network is moving rapidly toward TDM as the sole means of handling calls. Although there are still numerous FDM analog trunking systems installed, it is safe to say that the network, except for the final link from the local telephones to the central office, is rapidly becoming all-digital.

Myths About the Network

The telephone network has numerous myths associated with its operation. One basic myth is that the twisted pair cables installed between telephones and central offices are limited in their handling capacity to low speeds, such as 1,200 bps. Not so; twisted pair cables are capable of handling digital data rates of 1.54 million bits per second (M bps) and are used by the telephone industry to send signals at that rate, which is called T1 carrier. The Integrated Services Digital Network (ISDN), which is under development by the telephone industry today, will operate at a rate of 192K bps from the telephone to a central office switch, with 144K bps used for sending information and 48K bps used for diagnostic signalling and other administrative traffic. ISDN systems are already planned for implementation in selected trial cities in North America and will likely be implemented in every major city by the mid-1990s. It will be well into the 21st Century, however, before the entire telephone network is all-digital. Until then, the confusion about the ability of the telephone network to handle high data speeds is likely to continue.

The confusion about the data rates that today's network can handle extends to modems, which convert digital signals from computers and terminals into the analog wave forms required to travel over the telephone. When 300 bps modems were the standard in operation in the early 1970s and intensive efforts were underway to increase speeds to 1,200 bps, Bell System engineers were worried that the higher speed modems would not work on the public telephone network because of the technical limitations of step-by-step switching centers. The fears turned out to be unfounded, however, and modems have routinely increased in speed.

Today, it is commonplace to have modems communicate at 9,600 bps over the regular telephone network. Facsimile machines, for example, often use this rate. A number of companies, such as Microcom and Telebit, offer even faster modems at speeds up to 18K bps. Microprocessor and associated chip technologies are also dropping the cost barrier of low speed modems rapidly. In 1985, for example, a 1,200 bps modem was priced in the $350 to $500 range, and a 2,400 bps modem was priced at about $700 to $900. Today, 1,200 bps modems are as low as $100, and 2,400 bps modems are in the $300 to $500 range. Within two years, 2,400 or 4,800 bps modems are likely to be the common standard speed for low cost modems. It is also likely that the speed barrier for higher priced modems will crumble further, with speeds for a 56,000 bps modem falling to the $2,000 range. These modems will be based on using multiple frequencies to send digital signals, rather than two frequencies as used by most modems today.

The Telex Network

Telex is essentially a telephone system for low speed terminals that communicate at one of three speeds: 50, 75, or 200 bps. Telex terminals are connected to a central telex switch operated by the telex carrier via leased telephone lines that are provided by the local telephone company. The user dials the number of the receiver's telex machine, waits until a connection is made, receives an answerback—which is up to 23 letters that identify the receiving telex machine—and then sends the message. Interestingly, while telex sends its signals digitally, the network itself is largely analog, which is another reason why telex is outdated.

Users pay for telex on a per minute basis just as they do for long distance telephony. In the United States, the rate is about 46¢ per minute.

The Rise of Packet Switching

Packet switching networks consolidate multiple low speed devices onto single channels, allowing them to share the channels and the cost. The basic theory of packet switching is for multiple slow speed terminals to share the same telephone channel in such a way that each user thinks he has sole use of the channel. It is possible, for example, for dozens of terminals communicating at 300 bps to share the same channel by using multiplexers operating at 9,600 bps.

The idea of packet switching, interestingly, was born out of fear of a nuclear war, not an attempt to make the phone network more efficient. It was first conceived by Paul Baran in 1962 when he was working for the Rand Corporation on a project to devise a voice communications network for the U.S. Air Force that could survive a nuclear holocaust.[3] Voice and data switching networks at that time were based on the star concept, with a small number of large switches controlling the access to all of the terminals or telephones connected to the network. Should an atomic bomb hit the central switch, the network would cease to exist. In the Cold War atmosphere of the day, a major strategic goal of any war would be to wipe out the military's communications network. Thus, the U.S. Air Force initiated a project to devise a network that could survive such an attack.

Baran conceived a network that would consist of multiple switching nodes, each of which would be connected to at least two other nodes. Messages would be broken into modules and would travel through the network like "hot potatoes" being passed from node to node until they reached their final destination. One key to the network was that it would have no fixed connection pathway as does the circuit-switched telephone network. In Baran's envisioned network, each packet could take a different pathway, with the final message assembled at the last node. In this way, although some nodes might be wiped out by a nuclear blast, the overall network would be able to keep functioning.

Although Baran's idea was not considered practical for voice communications with the available technology, it was considered viable for data communications. In 1966, Don Davies, a researcher at the National Physics Laboratory in the United Kingdom, coined the term "packet" to describe the modules that would be created during his research. In 1968, DARPA funded the development of the live packet network called the ARPANET, and the first node was set up at UCLA in 1969. Overall the network was a huge success which led to Bolt, Baranek & Newman (BBN), the telecommunications engineering firm that had been involved with the project since its early stages, setting up the first operational CBMS for ARPANET in 1972. Today, the ARPANET is possibly the world's largest electronic mail network, connecting several thousand computers and hundreds of thousands of users.

While DARPA was doing its early work, timesharing and telephone companies also became interested in packet switching. Tymshare, in 1971, was the first commercial company to set up a packet switching network to handle traffic from its timesharing clients. And in 1974,

Dr. Lawrence Roberts, who had built the first CBMS while working for DARPA, started up the commercial packet network called Telenet, which has also become a huge success and was subsequently purchased by GTE. In 1976, The TransCanada Telephone System (now Telecom Canada) set up Datapac, the first publicly available packet switching network in North America (the first one in the world was set up in Spain). Today, there are some 15 public packet switching networks available in the United States and Canada, along with about 100 private networks operating within major corporations. Packet switching has become recognized as being more flexible and cost-effective than circuit switching to handle low speed communications between terminals and host computers.

Fundamental Elements of a Packet Network

There is nothing mysterious about packet switching networks, except for the terminology used to describe them. The most confusing is when packet networks are talked about as "virtual circuit networks". Basically, a packet network consists of five elements: the packet switching exchanges, a network control center, packet assemblers/disassemblers (PADs), remote multiplexers, and leased telephone channels. Packet switching begins and ends with the assembly and disassembly of packets, which consist of a header, the text, an error-detection mechanism, and a trailer that identifies the end of the packet. The header identifies the recipient of the packet (node and connection point); the error detection mechanism is used to determine that the information was received exactly as transmitted; and the trailer designates the end of the transmission.

The packets are then sent throughout the packet network from switch to switch until they reach their destination. Although Baran's concept was for each packet to take a different route based on available channels, most packet networks operate by setting up a specific route for all of the packets to travel during a session between a terminal and a host or between two host devices. Multiplexers are used to send the packets at high speeds between switches, which allows multiple low speed devices to share the network during their sessions as if they have a dedicated circuit connected between their terminal and the host. The Network Control Center monitors the operation of the network and allows nodes to be selectively activated and deactivated.

Concepts such as "virtual circuits" do more to confuse people than to explain what it is that packet switching networks do. These networks have developed elaborate communication protocols, which are standardized by the CCITT, to regulate the creation of packets and their flow throughout the network. The packet switching protocols defined by the CCITT, such as X.25, X.28, and X.29, regulate the transmission of packets between the switches and defined devices such as terminals and host computers. Although the CCITT has defined a series of packet switching protocols as part of its X-series, they are usually referred to as X.25, which is the protocol that defines the interface to packet networks.

The X-series protocols consist of parameters to make a connection at three communication "layers": the physical level, the link level, and the network connection level. Furthermore, packet switching networks are often used as a bridge between devices that communicate with different protocols. It is possible, for example, for a packet network to receive information from a terminal communicating in one protocol, such as IBM's SDLC, and encapsulate it with X.25's link protocol, HDLC, so that the information can be sent to an IBM host that understands X.25.

Figure 4-2 shows the structure of a typical packet network, which is overlayed on top of the public telephone network. The terminals and host computers, for example, are both connected to the packet switches through local telephone exchanges, although by different means. The hosts have dedicated, leased line connections from the host's location through the telephone switch to the packet network. The terminals either use the regular public telephone network to connect to dial-in ports operated by the packet switching vendor or they are also routed via dedicated, leased lines. The packet switches, in turn, are connected to primary long distance telephone switches. Packets are created either at the end user sites or in the packet switches, which consist of the switching elements and the packet creation elements. Packet networks also have a Network Control Center that is used to monitor the operation of the network.

Link Between Terminals and Hosts

At present, most terminals do not use the X.25 protocol. Instead, they call into devices that perform the basic PAD conversions before entry into the switches. In some cases, these PADs are located inside the packet switches. In other cases, they are located on the user's site. Recently, a number of companies have introduced add-on card devices that allow personal computers to communicate directly using X.25, which has prompted the public packet networks to set up public dial-in X.25 ports to handle such terminals.[4] Dial-up X.25 connections are defined under the X.32 protocol by the CCITT. Host computers, on the other hand, all communicate using the X.25 protocol.

Figure 4-2. Operation of a Packet Switching Network

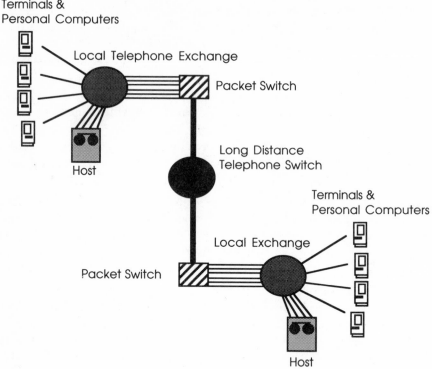

Packet Switching Access and Economics

Packet switching has been critical to the development of the CBMS part of the electronic mail industry because it has dramatically lowered the access to public CBMS services. The rates for long distance telephony, for example, are almost always based upon distance. A call of 100 miles may be 35¢ per minute whereas a cross-country call may be 60¢ per minute. Packet networks, because they can multiplex many terminals over one leased line, have considerably lower rates that average about 9¢ per minute. Packet networks also have a single nationwide rate for transmission, although they have two- or three-tiered hourly connection rates depending upon the user's access city. The rates range from about $4 to $12 per hour.

Packet vendors allow hosts to accept collect calls, which is another important element. This allows the public service to know the exact rate that it will be charged for every call it accepts. It also allows the callers to dial public local telephone numbers to reach any host on the network. The public service vendors then bundle the communications cost into their own charges. The result is that service suppliers can control their costs, and users have easy entry to their host computers. Had the economics been different, the electronic mail industry would have developed differently.

Today, the major packet switching networks are accessible via local calls from about 700 cities throughout North America and have a reach that covers more than 90 percent of the population. They have become the major roadways for the public electronic mail services and many private in-house systems.

Private Computer Networks

Although packet switching networks are the wave of the future, the installed bases of the present are typically connected via private computer networks, with IBM having by far the largest installed base of networks. At last count, there were more than 5 million terminals connected into IBM computer networks. IBM, furthermore, is not the only vendor with clients who operate large networks. Digital Equipment, Unisys, Data General, Hewlett-Packard, Prime, and Honeywell all have customer bases that operate extensive computer networks. Digital, in fact, claims to have the largest network in the world with close to 20,000 separate nodes. This makes private computer networks a major place to implement electronic mail systems. During the past five years, for example, CBMS-based electronic mail software has been added to thousands of mainframe and minicomputers on private networks, providing electronic mailboxes to literally a few million users. A number of large companies, furthermore, have already spread their electronic mail systems to tens of thousands of users. These companies include IBM, Digital Equipment, Procter & Gamble, Citibank, Texas Instruments, and Hewlett-Packard, just to name a few. There are also numerous companies that have a few thousand users on their mail system, representing from 5 to 50 percent of their employees. Such firms include Bankers Trust, Mutual of New York, Chrysler, and Ford. During the next few years, most companies that now have electronic mail systems in operation on their private computer networks will face the problem of expanding their mail systems from a small segment of their companies to the entire corporation.

Wide Area Networks

Wide area networks bypass the traditional telephone network to provide high speed communications capacity directly from a user's facility.

The most common wide area network is based on a satellite communications link between a number of different locations. Numerous major corporations, for example, now operate their own private satellite networks that provide them with point-to-point, high speed voice and data communications.

The advantage these networks bring is direct access to high data communication speeds that can be many megabytes of data per second. Wide area networks open the door to high speed electronic mail systems that go far beyond the scope and power of systems available today. One company, Satellite Business Systems (SBS), which was set up as a consortium of IBM, Aetna, and Comsat (but was sold to MCI Communications in 1985), designed a high speed electronic mail system that used facsimile to ship documents around the country at a page every half second. Interestingly, few, if any, of SBS' customers purchased the system, and there are none in use today. The system, however, remains a potential blueprint for high powered electronic mail systems of the future.

Local Area Networks

There are three types of local area networks: PBXs, in-house computer networks, and LANs. Although the PBX is often not thought of as a local area network, this is the precise function it performs for voice telephones. The in-house computer network typically connects terminals to only one mainframe computer, although it is becoming more common for terminals to have access to multiple mainframes on the same network. The third type of local area network, known as a LAN, connects personal computers and small workstations together at high speeds within a building. These LANs are also increasingly allowing intelligent workstations such as PCs to connect directly to minicomputers and mainframes.

For electronic mail, it is often far more difficult for people to interlink together inside a building than it is to reach a nationwide public service. This is because it is easy for most users to gain access to an outside telephone line, which is used to connect to a packet network. It can be very difficult and expensive for a company to install a network to interconnect people within one building. For example, although electronic-mail capability may only cost $200 to $300 per user, including a modem and telecommunications software, it can be two or three times that per user to set up a roadway inside the building to connect users together. In fact, there are many companies where employees dial from the company PBX through a central telephone office to reach computers installed on company premises instead of just going directly to the machine via a local area network.

PBX

The PBX is one of the most important elements in the electronic mail delivery chain. Access to public mail services, for example, is often via the company's PBX, with the PC operating with a modem and appearing to the PBX as a regular voice telephone call. Because of the growing percentage of installed digital PBXs that can be upgraded to handle integrated voice and data streams, furthermore, the PBX can become the means of accessing internal electronic mail services within the building (or campus). Digital PBXs, in fact, can handle both text-based CBMS and voice mailbox systems, although it is far easier to handle voice mail systems because telephones can be used as the input mechanism. Most PBXs already have numerous voice mail systems that are set up to work seamlessly with them, which means that the voice mail system can be set up as a telephone answering machine as well as a CBMS-style messaging system.

The choice of whether a PBX should be used as the roadway for an electronic mail system will depend upon the size of the organization, the level within the organization where electronic mail is planned for implementation, and the cost/capability of upgrading the PBX to handle both voice and data. If the company wants one central system for all its employees, for example, and has employees located in multiple facilities with numerous PBXs, then a single PBX is probably not a suitable vehicle. If the company wants a mail system primarily for people within one building or campus, however, then a PBX may be the best choice if it can handle both voice and data. Finally, if the company is large, with multiple facilities, and plans a true electronic mail network, the PBX can be a good vehicle for a number of electronic mail nodes, which can be networked together independently.

In-House Computer Network

The in-house computer network is usually based upon RS-232-C cables that have been strung within the building to handle the connection of terminals to a host computer at speeds up to 9,600 bps. In many cases, companies with multiple computers have installed data PBXs to switch the terminals to these different computers within the building. The big issue for in-house computer networks is whether they should be integrated with an advanced PBX, which is an organizational as well as a technical problem. In many companies, the people who administer the in-house computer network are different from the people who handle the telephone system. Getting them to plan together is often as big a problem as implementing any solution that might result.

LANs

LANs developed to move traffic locally at high speeds between computers, workstations, and peripherals. LANs operate at speeds of from 200K to 100M bps and are used typically to share resources at high speeds. A personal computer on a LAN, for example, can share a hard disk on a remote machine without the user knowing that the disk is not locally connected. LANs are also used to share other centralized resources, such as printers. Such resources are typically provided on servers, which are small computers dedicated to serving the needs of other machines on the network, although it is also possible to allow resources on every machine to be shared by other users.

LANs provide a unique environment for electronic mail that is very different from the other types of roadways. Packet switching networks, for example, can allow vast numbers of people together on a centralized mail system that can be accessed both nationwide and internationally. The 12 leading systems in North America, for example, now have more than 1 million users. Although the hosts are located in the United States, they can be reached from more than 70 countries worldwide via packet switching gateways. These services have also interconnected with the telex network and to offnet services such as postal services and couriers. This extends the reach of electronic mail services on packet networks worldwide.

LANs, however, typically have less than 20 users on them each and represent tiny dots within an overall organization. Electronic mail software for LANs typically focuses on the users within the LAN, allowing mixed-media messages to be communicated. Most electronic mail LAN software can also be networked, although typically only with LANs that run the same electronic mail package. The reality of LANs changes corporate electronic mail strategies, whether planners like it or not, by making it far more difficult to adopt a centralized electronic mail system. When LANs proliferate inside a company, some type of multinode electronic mail network is a necessity, which means that electronic mail LAN software must be capable of network interaction.

Importance of Electronic Mail Architecture

The roadways that are available for electronic mail all have very different characteristics and cost structures. The choice of which type of roadway to use, however, is usually less complex than might be imagined. Companies will tilt toward using their existing roadways as much as possible to avoid the high capital costs of building new communication networks. Planners, however, cannot jump to the conclusion that existing networks are the only choice. Until the scope of the electronic mail network is clear, a planner should keep an open mind about the type of network that will be required.

Regardless of theory, implementing systems usually boils down to making dozens of separate decisions on how to meet immediate user needs. This is especially true now that small LANs are proliferating at rapid rates. In this type of environment, it is critical that electronic mail planners develop an overall architecture for their electronic mail network, so that they have a framework in which to make both the strategic and tactical decisions that will inevitably arise. Without an architecture, each decision will end up being made upon existing budgets and operational requirements without reference to any long-range plan. As anyone who has followed the development of the U.S. automobile industry during the past 30 years knows, the results of making constant short-term decisions without regard to a long-term architecture can end up in disaster.

An electronic mail architecture, incidentally, is required by both public service and private, in-house system users, especially as it is becoming commonplace for large and small companies to have both in-house systems and public services. As an example, Chrysler has its headquarters and regional management on a PROFs system operated on a nationwide computer network but has its sales force and dealers on a public service. The PROFs system is interconnected to the public service, Geisco's Quik-Comm, so that both groups can communicate.

It is possible for even a tiny company with 10 to 20 employees to have both an in-house system and public service. The in-house mail system may operate on a LAN, and the public service may be used to communicate to customers and suppliers. Although users in the small company may have mailboxes on both the LAN and the public service and call each independently, in the future, it may be advantageous to connect the LAN directly to the public service so that all communications are moved to the mailbox at the LAN.

The key point, however, is that unless electronic mail planners take a broad look at the strategic directions of the company and plan an architecture that meets those goals, decisions will inevitably be made based on short-term needs. Although this may work fine for many companies, it may also end up with the company not being able to meet longer term goals without expensive changes to the existing system(s).

X.400

X.400 is the white knight of electronic mail that promises to allow both public and private multinode mail networks to develop on a global basis. For electronic mail planners and top executives, understanding X.400 is important because of its strategic implications for electronic mail networks.

The availability of X.400 systems changes the entire electronic mail game because it provides planners with an internationally standardized interconnection architecture that should greatly simplify the confusing decisions in interconnecting message systems. The specifics of X.400 for planning electronic mail networks are explored in more detail in Chapter 12 on developing electronic mail networks. This chapter explores the basic implications of X.400 as an electronic mail architecture.

X.400 was developed by the CCITT, which, as was noted earlier, is the standards-setting body of the International Telecommunications Union. The development of X.400 is closely related to the Open Systems Interconnection (OSI) standards under development within the International Standards Organization (ISO). X.400 and OSI have their roots in work done in the late 1970s inside the International Federation of Information Processing (IFIP). The computer companies took this work into the ISO, whereas their communications brethren went to the CCITT. Figure 4-3 shows the OSI seven-layer model.

X.400, in essence, is an implementation of the seventh layer of the OSI model, specifying how messages can be exchanged between specific users (or computer applications). Although the basic concept that underlies X.400 is simple, the X.400 protocols themselves can seem foreign because they introduce a new set of terminology that describes the process. X.400, however, is easy to understand when explained functionally in relationship to the OSI model. The most important point to understand is that each layer of the model operates independently of the other layers. X.400, for example, defines an application at the seventh layer. It is possible to operate an X.400 mail system over any type of communication roadway, which is typically defined within the first three layers of the model.

The physical layer (1) handles physical wiring and connectors that allow terminals and workstations to transmit bits of information. The RS-232-C standard, for example, identifies the physical pin structure used to connect a terminal to a communications device, such as a modem. The link layer (2) specifies the actual handshaking routines used to coordinate the transfer of these bits. In effect, the link layer specifies how the data is passed over the specific connector pins identified at the physical layer. As might be expected, different link level protocols exist because of the many different patterns that can be used. The network layer (3) specifies how these bits are transferred to and from the network. The X.25 packet switching protocol, for example, specifies packet addressing and handling at the third OSI layer. The transport layer (4) specifies an end-to-end protocol for inter-process communications. End-to-end file transfer with error detection-correction would be identified at this layer. Issues at layer 4 include flow control and retransmission sequencing in the event of transfer errors. The session layer (5) specifies how two intelligent devices conduct a session together, including issues such as establishing a session and recovering from terminating a session. The presentation layer (6) deals with issues of how the information is presented to both the sender and receiver. This is where format conversions between non-compatible files are performed. The application layer (7) deals with the specific application being performed, such as a transfer of an electronic mail message between a sender and a recipient. It is at this layer where the system handles tasks such as determining whether the address of the recipient is proper, whether the recipient can handle the file being sent, and what types of error or confirmation messages to send based upon the request from the sending system.

Figure 4-3. OSI Model of Communications

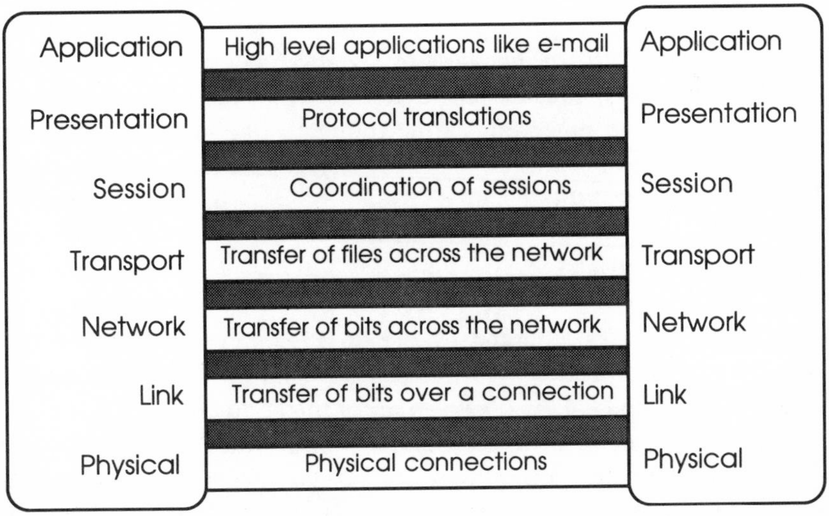

Application	High level applications like e-mail	Application
Presentation	Protocol translations	Presentation
Session	Coordination of sessions	Session
Transport	Transfer of files across the network	Transport
Network	Transfer of bits across the network	Network
Link	Transfer of bits over a connection	Link
Physical	Physical connections	Physical

X.400's terminology is based upon the concepts of software agents that perform the various functions of a message system. The User Agent (UA) handles processing tasks for specific users, whereas the

Message Transfer Agent (MTA) handles the transmission of messages between two systems. Because the UA and MTA are separate software entities, they can exist within a single computer or on separate computers. Thus, it is possible to have a computer that performs both UA and MTA functions or to have computers that handle only one of these functions.

Roadway Building Blocks

X.400 is a set of building blocks for an electronic-mail network, with the standards at one level capable of being mixed and matched with standards at lower layers. It is possible, for example, to implement X.400 over a telephone network, with mail systems connected via leased lines at 9,600 bps rates; over a packet network, with hosts connected via the X.25 protocol; or over a LAN with coaxial cables and a transmission rate of 10M bps. If bridges are built between two different networks, furthermore, such as a packet network and a LAN, then the X.400 software on both the LAN's file server and the packet network's host should have no trouble exchanging messages and other files.

X.400 can also gateway to existing architectures, such as IBM's DISOSS or SNADS, both of which are proprietary protocols developed by IBM that allow individual users to exchange messages and files. Gateways allow companies to implement X.400 in some parts of their network or to communicate to other networks without having to convert every system in the network to a native X.400 implementation. Given the possibility that no single architecture will meet the needs of even medium-sized companies, the ability to use gateways between different architectures will almost certainly be one of the more popular strategies in the future.

Availability of X.400

When X.400 was first adopted by the CCITT, many people thought it would be the early 1990s before X.400 systems were available on the market. Surprise has always been a part of this industry, and X.400 has been one of the more pleasant. Commercial X.400 gateways are now available on the market from more than a dozen companies, including Digital Equipment, Telenet, Data General, AT&T, Dialcom, Telecom Canada, and Hewlett-Packard. Telenet is already providing conformance testing in the United States between its X.400 implementation and other implementations. The Corporation for Open Systems, whose charter is to provide testing for OSI protocols, also plans to

provide conformance testing in 1988. Conformance testing is important for X.400 because it will measure whether a specific vendor's implementation matches the international standard.

Limitations of X.400

In short, X.400 is now here in the market as a means of connecting
incompatible mail systems. X.400, however, has some considerable
limitations. In particular, the present X.400 version has no
standardized directory structure that would allow directory services to
be provided across different networks. In addition, only a small
number of the many mail systems on the market have X.400 available.
IBM, however, plans to deliver an X.400 gateway in 1988. Thus,
although the first implementations of X.400 are on the market, there
is still a long way to go before companies can buy off-the-shelf X.400
mail networks and easily interconnect their mail systems from
different vendors.

Telematic Services

In Chapter 3, seven types of electronic mail technologies were described:

- Telex I & II;
- Facsimile;
- Communicating word processors and teletex;
- Personal computers;
- Computer-based message systems;
- Computer conferencing systems; and
- Voice mail systems.

During the past several years, the first three— telex I & II, facsimile, and communicating word processors and teletex— have become known as telematic services, which is a term that comes from the CCITT. All three of these services are presently being integrated by the CCITT Study Group VIII. This chapter describes these electronic mail systems in more detail.

Telex I & II

Because of the regulatory environment that controlled telecommunications until the last four years, there are a relatively small number of suppliers of telex I & II services, the leaders of whom were once part of what was called the "old boy network" in telex. There are also numerous organizations that operate their own private wire telex-based networks. To give an example, numerous airlines have private wire networks for their maintenance and baggage operations.

Domestic Competition

In the United States, there are six companies that operate public telex networks: Western Union, RCA Global Communications, ITT World

Communications, MCI International, Graphic Scanning, and TRT Telecommunications. All these firms operate as International Record Carriers (IRCs) that handle overseas telex traffic. In Canada, domestic telex is handled by CNCP Telecommunications, and international telex is handled by Teleglobe Canada. Telecom Canada operates a TWX (telex II) network in Canada with 4,000 terminals, most of which are inside the telecommunications industry. In all, there are about 200,000 telex I & II terminals connected to the public network in the United States and 40,000 telex terminals in Canada.

The Telex Pirates

Until the last few years, telex was an oligopoly. Western Union operated the domestic telex network in the United States, and the IRCs handled overseas telex, although Western Union had 25,000 terminals connected directly to the international networks. The same was true in Canada. Telex rates were also quite high. A typical rate was $2.40 per minute to most European countries.

In the late 1970s, a number of companies took advantage of newer telecommunication services to cut into the overseas telex market. These companies set up minicomputers in major gateway cities, such as New York, and collected message traffic from customers looking for a price break. They then took the telex messages, batched them together and sent them via the voice telephone network or packet networks to a minicomputer set up in the United Kingdom, which then refiled them into the telex network at European rates, which are similar to North American rates.

These telex refilers, which were called pirate carriers by the IRCs, undercut international telex rates by as much as 80 percent and succeeded in capturing a small, but significant, percentage of the market, typically in high volume users. Although the IRCs complained to the FCC about the pirates, the FCC made no move to stop what were apparently illegal activities. Although it has never been stated, it is believed that the FCC looked favorably on the telex refilers as a natural means of policing overseas telex rates, which have subsequently plummeted from $2.40 per minute to $1.82.

In 1982, the FCC ended the battle between the IRCs and the budding telex refiling industry by deregulating international telex traffic. Western Union took advantage of this and jumped into the international telex business, and the IRCs, which had 25,000 terminals connecting directly to them in gateway cities, opened these up to domestic traffic. The "pirates", in turn, became legitimate international record carriers.

Today, the telex industry is considerably more confusing than it was a decade ago, but it also is far more competitive and cost-effective. In less than a decade, the price for sending international telex messages has dropped from $2.40 per minute to Europe to as low as $1.20 per minute when using telex refilers. In addition to Western Union, Graphic Scanning, and the IRCs, there are more than 50 companies that offer telex refiling services, with the leading firm being CCI, Inc. (New York City), which is owned jointly by Telenet and the British firm, Aircall.

Benefits and Applications

Telex has been much maligned as a technologically outdated service, but it does have three major benefits:

- Directory of users worldwide;
- Delivery to a specific terminal in writing; and
- Well-known operation procedures within companies that assure message delivery.

These benefits make telex a highly effective communications medium because of its reliability and availability. Furthermore, although telex is expensive in comparison to other electronic mail networks, it is still cost-effective from the overall picture of delivering a critical message. It is far faster, for example, than sending a message via overnight courier service and oftentimes more effective than a telephone call, which is limited by differences in both time zones and language.

The issue of language is particularly important for telex. In North America, for example, which has a relatively low cost voice telephone system, along with one language spoken by most people in business, telex plays a minor role in communications. In Europe, however, which has multiple languages, telex plays a far more significant role in businesses and is a highly effective means of delivering an important message to a recipient.

In Europe, telex is used to deliver messages that are typically related to the transfer of money or the movement of goods within and between organizations. Numerous shippers, for example, use telex to send notices about the status of goods in transit. It is also used between suppliers to place orders and ask for information. Telex is also used to send personal messages, such as confirmations and information related to travel plans or general requests for information. Most companies in Europe have people who will translate telexes into the appropriate language for the intended recipient.

Although telex is used for the same types of money transfer, shipping, ordering, and inventory applications within North America, it is rarely used to communicate personal information. Most people prefer the convenience of using the telephone, which is on their desk, rather than taking the time to send a telex. In fact, something like 70 percent of the telexes originated in North America are destined for overseas. Applications for telex in North America are typically related to the movement of goods between shippers and receivers.

Store-and-Forward Traffic

Today, the major decision point for a planner in telex is whether the messages can go via store-and-forward or whether they must be sent in real-time. Store-and-forward traffic can easily be moved from the higher priced IRCs to a telex refiler, whereas traffic that must go in real-time will have to remain on one of the existing IRC networks.

This has significant implications for planning decisions because of the way in which telex is organized in most companies. Telex is typically provided as a centralized service from the communications center, with the sender writing or typing out the telex on a form and having it hand-carried to the telex room. It is then put in a queue for either high priority or regular delivery, retyped, and then sent out as a telex. The telex machines were once clunkers made exclusively by Teletype Corp.; today there is a strong trend toward integrated message terminals that have CRT screens, full-screen editors, and the ability to interface into telex and ASCII networks.

The modern telex machines, from firms such as Sidereal, Extel, and Teletype Corp., have significantly improved productivity inside the telex room itself, but they do not get to the core issue in planning for telex: whether to decentralize the transmission point for telexes. In applications where real-time transmission and security are important, such as a bank that is using telex to transfer funds, the centralization and control of the transmission is critical. But for many telexes, the main issue is reliable delivery. The means— store-and-forward or real-time— is not important. This opens up the option for planners to move these messages out of the communications center to the departments that create them. Assuming that most departments have PCs, it is possible for the telexes to be written on them and sent to a store-and-forward service or to a CBMS service, virtually all of which interface into the telex network. Another important factor is the ease of planning. Because the communications center knows the originators of the telexes, it is easy to perform volume samples to determine which departments should handle telexes directly versus which departments should be served by the centralized communications room.

Cost savings are also easy to determine. Each telex that is written on a special form and then hand-carried to the telex room and retyped has a number of shadow function costs associated with its production that go well beyond the transmission cost. The telex must be carried by a runner, who may take 10 to 15 minutes for the delivery. Then the telex must be logged into the communications center and rekeyed, which may take another 10 minutes. In all, although it may only cost $3 to send the telex, handling it may cost an additional $5. If telexes are decentralized to their point of creation, all these shadow functions are eliminated without giving up control of centralized cost tracking because the telex providers all have billing mechanisms that allow for departmental billing codes to be entered with each message.

Telex Operations

Store-and-forward telex operations are not exactly what one would call "user-friendly", which is one of the reasons why they are not suitable to

Figure 5-1. Example of Using Store-and-Forward Telex System

RCA Telextra
Your ID PLS?
232323 USER CD

July 18 1567 746534
GA MSGS

345345+
This is a typical telex message
sent via a store-and-forward telex
system.
NNNN
728945+
This is the second message, which is
sent in the same batch and is separated
by NNNN at the beginning of the line

.....

RCVD 994567
RCVD 994568

be decentralized throughout an entire organization, although they can certainly be moved to departments with significant message volumes. In fact, the operation of store-and-forward telex fits Thomas Hobbes' description of life in the 16th Century as "nasty, brutish and short". The services are available via direct dial telephone lines, typically 800 numbers, and have a very terse command structure, which is shown for RCA's Telextra service below in Figure 5-1 (the system prompts are in boldface, and the user responses are in italics).

All the store-and-forward systems work in similar fashion, with a few variations in the codes. In general, "GA" means ready to send, "NNNN" means end of message, and "LLLL" means send this message and let me send another. Addressing is also esoteric. For example, if a message cannot be delivered to the first address specified, an alternate can be chosen by a double slash "//" before another address beneath the original.

To sum up, telex is very primitive, yet effective for those who take the time to learn its shorthand. These systems also require accurate typing because they do not have editors on their systems. If a message is mistyped, it must be re-entered, which is why all telex operators work on terminals with offline editors.

Communicating Word Processors and Teletex

When the word processing industry was in its heyday in the late 1970s and early 1980s, the demand for communications — at least for the availability of communications — was strong. Usage, however, turned out to be low. Today, most CWPs are installed for specific applications, with the strongest area of support in the legal community. It is a classic case of technology creating a solution and then looking around for problems to solve.

Teletex evolved in a very different manner. It was the brainchild of the telecommunications industry looking for an upgrade to telex. Because word processing was catching on strongly, it made sense to merge the two and kill two birds with one stone— an upgrade to telex and a document content standard. Its formal CCITT definition is as follows:

> Teletex is an international service, offered by administrations or recognized private operating agencies (RPOAs), enabling subscribers to exchange correspon-

dence on an automatic memory-to-memory basis via
telecommunications networks.

The keys to teletex are its adherence to CCITT recommendations at
different telecommunication layers, a directory of users, and a special
character set that is a superset of most other key character sets now
available, including ASCII, EBCDIC, and Baudot. The character set can
be used to print messages in 37 languages that use the Latin alphabet
and can also be used for transliteration into 31 other languages that do
not use a Latin alphabet. Because teletex machines are designed to be
operated within public services, it is up to the telecommunications
administration to define the network that the teletex machines will
operate on. Most have opted to have teletex ride on specialized circuit-switched data networks, such as CNCP Telecommunications in
Canada, although a few telecommunications agencies, such as Telecom
Canada, have opted for the public telephone network. At this writing,
there are more than 30 countries that have set up teletex services or
are in the process of doing so.

Planning Issues for CWPs and Teletex

For an electronic mail planner, the question is whether there is any
role, other than a minor one, for either CWPs or teletex. Word processors are declining in the market, so the question in word processing
is how to integrate the existing installed base with the growing base of
PCs into an overall document delivery network. This makes the CWP
issue a subset of the far more complex issue of document distribution
inside a large organization, which is enough to turn anyone's hair gray.
The basic problem is that the base of workstations is growing far faster
than the ability to put up roadways, which is the automobile analogy
with a perverse twist: everyone buying cars before there are any roads.

For teletex, the issue is much simpler. Teletex should be viewed
within the context of international telecommunications needs. If present international telex patterns justify switching from telex to teletex,
then the move makes sense. It is not a good move, however, to invest
in teletex because it may become an important technology. A much
more likely pathway will be for computer-based message switching
systems to integrate with teletex, much as they have with telex, so
that a user will be able to send a document to a CBMS, which will convert it to teletex format and deliver it to the small base that does
evolve.

Facsimile

Facsimile has been on a rapid growth curve since the Japanese began their heavy developmental work in the mid-1970s. Facsimile is particularly important to the Japanese because the ideological character set of their language is not well suited to keyboarded characters. In less than a decade, the Japanese have revamped the technology and have largely merged it with the copying and laser printing industries, all of which now use similar printing subsystems, but different input systems.

CCITT Group Facsimile Standards

The key to facsimile's growth has been the Group 1, 2, 3, and 4 facsimile recommendations adopted by the CCITT as the T-series of standards. The Group 1 and 2 recommendations were based on analog machines developed in the late 1960s and early 1970s by Xerox and Graphic Sciences that sent pages at a rate of 3 to 6 minutes or 2 to 4 minutes per page respectively. Graphic Sciences, as noted earlier, was purchased by Burroughs in the mid-1970s, which sold the operation to Fujitsu in 1986.

In 1980, the CCITT adopted the Group 3 standard, which specifies transmission at 20 seconds per page when using 9,600 bps modems. The standard was supported heavily by the Japanese, who invested heavily in the facsimile industry. In Japan, facsimile is the major means of sending electronic mail. During the past five years, the price of Group 3 facsimile machines has plummeted from above $10,000 to as low as $1,500, which has changed the facsimile industry entirely.

The Group 4 facsimile recommendation was initially intended to specify transmission at 5 seconds per page and has not yet been finalized by the CCITT. The likely standard, however, is well known and already implemented by a number of vendors. The problem with the intended Group 4 recommendation is not the facsimile technology but the available roadways. To obtain its speed per page, Group 4 facsimile requires a 56,000 bps transmission rate, which is not yet widely available over the public telephone network. For this reason, the final CCITT recommendation will most likely specify the digital compression technique, page resolutions, and communications protocol between machines, but will not specify the transmission rate.

To get a basic idea of Group 4 facsimile, the resolution will be set at 300 x 300 lpi (lines per inch), with an optional resolution of 400 x 400 lpi. The compression technique is known as modified Huffman. It is based on the Huffman compression technique used in Group 3 machines. The rate of speed will vary from 4,800 bps to as high as digital networks will allow. The resolution, incidentally, is the same as that used in low cost laser printers now used in the desktop publishing industry, which means that Group 4 facsimile machines will be capable of transmitting almost typeset quality documents.

Benefits and Applications

Today, there are close to 900,000 Group 3 digital facsimile machines installed in North America, according to export statistics from Japan's Ministry of Trade & Industry (MITI). The applications for facsimile are far more diverse than those for telex because of the ability to transmit copies of an original page. Although the quality of transmission in early facsimile machines was poor, with a resolution of 96 lpi, the resolution of Group 3 machines is quite acceptable as copies, with a resolution of 200 lpi. The higher quality Group 3 machines also have an optional 300 lpi mode.

This opens the door to the use of facsimile as a replacement for the regular mails when the time factor in transmitting a document— especially one with graphics or a signature—between two or three locations is important. This makes facsimile a general-purpose electronic mail system that is well suited for operation within almost any department of an organization. Most companies that purchase facsimile machines, in fact, have created a network that is open to use by all departments. It should be kept in mind, however, that when an electronic mail device is out of sight, it is often out of mind. Thus, many of these machines are vastly under-utilized simply because people forget that they are available, even when the need is critical. The chances are very high that usage of facsimile would double or triple if the machines were more visible.

A number of companies have gone far beyond general-purpose usage and use facsimile for very specialized applications. Boeing (Seattle, Wash.), for example, is often cited as the nation's leading user of facsimile because it requires that all its engineering changes between departments and subcontractors be sent via Group 3 facsimile machines.

Boeing's usage shows how electronic mail can be a strategic technology. Its use is not designed to save money, but to eliminate the time delays associated with courier services and the mails. In Boeing's application, for example, every change order reaches its destination one day faster than otherwise, which saves millions of dollars in staff time alone by notifying people of changes one day sooner.

The major benefit of facsimile is the time it saves in delivering documents from one place to another, especially when graphics are required. The potential is phenomenal. A typical digital facsimile machine is in the $2,500 to $4,000 range ($120 per month over a three-year period). This makes facsimile easy to cost justify with a specific application such as Boeing's. The cost of using courier service is likely to be as high.

Facsimile is particularly important because it can handle graphics as well as text. As might be expected, graphics-oriented departments and industries, such as advertising and engineering, are already heavy users of facsimile. But its use should also extend into general business departments as well, particularly for sending copies of invoices and other form-related material. Facsimile is also useful for sending copies of presentations and reports to people with a need to review them in advance. In these applications, it is the value-added opportunity that justifies facsimile, not its potential cost savings. How important is it to have a key member of a team take a look at a presentation in advance? It could make the difference between a proposal being accepted or rejected.

There is one more important point concerning facsimile for an electronic mail planner. Facsimile may be the most effective of all the electronic mail technologies because it is easy to integrate into a present business operation and has some very clear cost justifications. Unlike a CBMS, which requires considerable training of new users, a facsimile machine is almost as easy to operate as a copier.

Facsimile Systems and Services

Most facsimile machines are either leased or purchased for use within corporations. In the past, Group 1 and 2 machines were typically operated at the departmental level, whereas Group 3 machines were operated in central communications centers. Today, it is increasingly common for departments to procure their own Group 3 machines directly, especially as machines are now available for as low as $1,500. The leading suppliers of facsimile machines, in alphabetical order, are AT&T, Canon, Fujitsu, Nippon Electric (NEC), Panasonic, Pitney Bowes, Ricoh, Sanyo, Sharp, Telautograph, 3M, and Xerox. Interestingly, the industry has changed almost overnight from domination by large U.S. office machine suppliers such as Burroughs, Pitney Bowes, 3M, and Xerox into a free-wheeling market that is increasingly being controlled by Japanese manufacturers. Even the large U.S. firms are no more than distribution chains for the Japanese manufacturers, which sell their equipment wholesale. AT&T, for example, buys its facsimile equipment from Ricoh. As almost formal testimony of Japanese domination, Fujitsu recently purchased Burroughs' facsimile operations.

From the user's viewpoint, this turns facsimile into a commodity market. Although the hardware once mattered a great deal because machines from different vendors would not talk to each other, today all of the machines intercommunicate. Thus, the major reasons for choosing a specific supplier are more related to service and price than to compatibility— and even service is becoming less important. Today's typical facsimile machine is arguably the most reliable piece of office equipment that can be installed. Most Group 3 facsimile machines use solid-state thermal printing mechanisms and electronic scanners; so, the only parts that move are the rollers that pull paper by the input scanner and print head. Typical mean time-to-failure for a facsimile machine is about 4,000 hours, which is the equivalent of 12,000 pages of transmission. With typical usage patterns of 400 pages per month, it is possible to operate a modern facsimile machine for 2.5 years without the need for repairs.

Transmission and Hardware Costs

There are three components to facsimile: the cost of the machine, the cost of the transmission, and the shadow functions to make a transmission. Facsimile machines use the public dial telephone network or private, in-house telephone networks to send pages. When transmitting facsimile pages took 6 minutes each, the cost could run very high to send a 10-page document, especially when operator times were added. Such a document could cost $30 in telephone costs, plus an hour of staff time for both the sender and receiver, each of whom required someone to babysit the machines to change paper after each page. When all the costs were considered, sending a 10-page document could cost a company $50 plus machine costs. Today, however, even the low end facsimile models have automatic page feeders and auto-answer capabilities; so, the sender only has to put the pages in a hopper and dial the receiving machine's number, with the rest being automatic. Sending a 10-page document is reduced from 1 hour to 4 minutes, with the transmission cost dropping from $30 to about $1.50. If the company has sufficient volume, this can bring the cost of using facsimile to far below the cost of a courier service, as is shown in Figure 5-2.

The comparison assumes a $4,000 facsimile machine that is written off over a 36-month period, which makes its cost about $135 per month. The break-even point is 12 transactions per month. At that volume, a courier service (Federal Express at $12.50 per transaction) would cost $150 for delivery, whereas using facsimile would cost $151.80. This makes it easy for numerous companies and departments to justify facsimile on cost alone, without even considering the value-added benefit of time savings.

Figure 5-2. Comparison of Facsimile to Courier Delivery

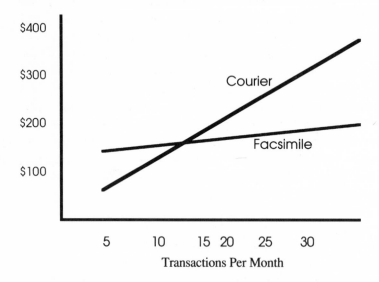

Readers should keep in mind that the break-even point for a facsimile versus courier service analysis will vary depending upon the cost of the facsimile machine and the volume discounts available from the courier service. Thus, planners will have to redo the basic math for any specific application in their organization. It should also be kept in mind that facsimile is only as effective as the willingness of people to use it. Unless the existence of the fax machine is well publicized, for example, and some attempt is made to promote usage, it is very possible for people to keep on using a courier out of habit, even though facsimile is faster and less expensive.

Connection to Computers

Facsimile is moving into the computer arena as well, although the connections are at their early stages. Minicomputer manufacturer Tandem Computer, for example, has introduced a product that allows a Group 3 facsimile machine to send and receive transmission from its computers. IBM also has a non-standard facsimile machine that can be integrated into its System Network Architecture (SNA). The unit is designed to allow text created on IBM Displaywrite word processors to be accompanied by graphics pages sent by IBM's facsimile machine.

Because of IBM's SNA, however, its facsimile machine is not compatible with Group 3 facsimile machines.

PCs are also getting into the act via add-on hardware boards that turn IBM or Macintosh PCs into the equivalent of Group 3 facsimile machines, enabling them to send and receive facsimile pages. Already, there are more than a dozen companies with fax cards, including some of the mainstream fax vendors such as Panasonic and Ricoh and newcomers such as Electronic Information Technologies (Fairfield, N.J.) and Brooktrout Technologies (Wellesley, Mass.). This level of integration, however, is at the transmission level, not at the applications level. Facsimile documents cannot easily be received by a computer and converted into machine-readable ASCII codes that can be edited by a word processor, although the first such products are now on the market. Electronic Information Technology, for example, has a fax card that will also perform OCR on fax documents that contain OCR fonts. Although such a capability seems attractive enough, it is still not clear how the market will react to such capabilities.

What is clear is that facsimile will play an increasingly important role inside electronic mail networks. Today, integration exists at the hardware level. During the next few years, integration will move to the directory level so that CBMS users will be able to send files to the growing network of facsimile machines throughout their organizations.

Group 4 Integration

Although CCITT facsimile Group recommendations 1 to 3 are separate standards for facsimile transmission alone, the Group 4 recommendation is part of the integration of telematic services now being developed by CCITT Study Group VIII.[1] Facsimile is being formally integrated into the teletex recommendations that were created in 1980. This will result in an international standard for integrated text/image documents. The problem with this recommendation is that the world may not follow it. CCITT recommendations typically have the force of a standard in the telecommunications industry where the CCITT has enormous authority. In computer-communications arenas, however, the recommendations are only adopted if the hardware and software manufacturers choose to follow them. This was the case in facsimile because the key hardware manufacturers, the Japanese, pushed for the recommendations. The key developers of word processing hardware and software, however, have politely ignored the CCITT; so, it is doubtful that any integrated text/image recommendation will be followed unless users literally force vendors to adopt it through purchasing power.

Teletex is a perfect example. Most manufacturers of word processing equipment have publically adopted the teletex standard; so, it is possible to buy devices that convert from the vendor's internal word processing format to the teletex file format. None of these vendors, however, actively market these devices in North America, and few actively market their devices in Europe. If a customer wants a teletex machine, it can be made available; but, there has been little effort by word processing manufacturers to push teletex.

Regardless of the outcome of facsimile's integration with teletex systems, Group 4 facsimile will be integrated with copiers and laser printers. Group 3 facsimile machines almost universally use thermal paper for printing. Group 4 machines, however, will use the same plain paper engines that are now available in small copiers such as the Canon Personal Copier and laser printers such as the Hewlett-Packard Laserjet and the Apple LaserWriter. All these machines use printing mechanisms that perform different functions, depending upon the electronics that drive them. If the engine has a copier "head", it is a copier. If it has a fiber-optic interface to a computer, it is a laser printer. If it has a telecommunications interface and document scanner, it is a facsimile machine.

This movement has already started in North America. Nippon Electric has introduced the first integrated facsimile/copier, although it is based upon a Group 3 machine. It is likely that typical office copiers of the future will come with the ability to be upgraded to facsimile machines, and vice versa.

Computer Message Systems

Computer-based Message Systems (CBMS) were first developed by computer researchers working on the ARPANET and in leading edge computer user organizations. Although the initial purpose was to exchange messages with other researchers, the task quickly became more sophisticated and turned into a programming exercise to emulate two environments:

- The Inbox-Outbox-Desktop-Filing environment of knowledge workers; and
- The message delivery capabilities of a postal system.

The Inbox-Outbox-Desktop-Filing environment models how knowledge workers operate at their desks. Memos taken from the inbox are read and then acted upon, which means some combination of the memo being replied to, forwarded, filed, or thrown away. Memos that are created are placed in the outbox for delivery.

The message delivery environment models how a postal system operates. Messages can be delivered via regular mail, which means placed into the inbox of the intended recipient(s), or messages can be sent with a number of different options, such as registered receipt, urgent, or acknowledgement. In addition, CBMS also can connect to the outside world, such as the telex network, regular postal system, courier services, or other CBMS, via gateways. The model of a typical CBMS is shown in Figure 6-1.

CBMS Functionality

The description in Figure 6-1 adequately categorizes the overall functionality of virtually every CBMS on the market, although no two systems have the same set of features or implement them in the same way. They also do not use the same nomenclature. In fact, there will be numerous synonyms used on different systems for the commands identified in this section. The only parts of a CBMS that are common to every system on the market are the inbox, which shows a listing of mail that can be read, and some message delivery environment, which transfers messages between users.

Figure 6-1. Model of a Typical CBMS

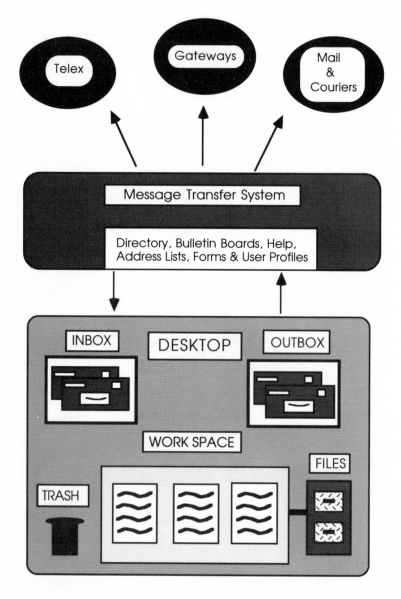

Many systems, for example, do not have outboxes or even filing systems. A few do not have editors, which are operated in the user's work space. Some systems, on the other hand, have all of the structures, including an inbox that shows new mail, a desktop that shows mail that has been read, an outbox that shows mail that has been sent, and a work space that is used to create and edit messages. These overall functions also tell only a part of the story about CBMS, most of which have numerous ways to manipulate messages inside the system. Most systems, for example, give users the ability to create address lists, which short-cuts having to type in the names of multiple recipients every time a message is sent to a specific group. The more powerful systems also allow users to create electronic business forms, which are specially formatted messages that prompt users for specific responses when creating the message; they also have bulletin boards so that messages can be posted to pre-defined groups. Finally, some systems can handle more types of files than the standard text files that are handled by all systems.

The Sign-On

The first, and sometimes hardest, step to using a CBMS is the sign-on, which requires the user to log on to the CBMS. If users are hardwired to the computer, this is simple because the electronic mail portion of the system will be available as part of an overall menu structure. Connecting to a remote CBMS, however, can be difficult because of the numerous parameters associated with sending data over a telecommunications network. As this is not a how-to book on using a CBMS, the intricacies of accessing remote systems are not discussed.

Upon reaching the CBMS, the user is asked to enter an ID and password, which are the major elements of security for any remote CBMS. On some systems, the IDs are based on the users' names; on others, they are numbers. Passwords are typically assigned by the administrator initially, with the users instructed to change their passwords to their own choice during the first sign on, although a number of public services now either choose the passwords for the users permanently or require that chosen passwords be minimum lengths and/or combinations of letters and numbers. Some systems, furthermore, now automatically require their users to change their passwords every few weeks. This is for security. If left to their own devices, many people choose simple passwords, which are easy for hackers to guess; thus, many system operators now require their users to enter more complex passwords.

The choice of whether to assign IDs as numbers or names is a significant one. Though assigning numbers is the most secure method, the most user-friendly choice is to make the ID similar to the way people are normally referred to via memos inside the organization.

Numerous companies, for example, have an informal convention, such as the first two initials and last name. When introducing a CBMS into a company, it helps if this convention can be carried over to the IDs. In this way, if the user wants to send a message to someone, but does not know the ID, it is easy to guess what it will be.

After successfully signing on, the user is then greeted with a welcome message, along with systemwide information. The public services, for example, usually have news summaries if they carry any wire service data bases. They will also have technical information about maintenance. Finally, they will provide information about any new features that have been added. Private systems will usually have less information in the header, and it will be more personal to the company. Here is an example of a typical screen after signing on:

> Welcome to ABC Company's Electronic Mail System
>
> The system will be taken down for maintenance from 12 pm to 6 am this Tuesday.
>
> Please check the company bulletin board for details on the new product introduced yesterday.
>
> You have new mail.
>
> Command?

Once a user gets past the sign-on stage into a CBMS, there are still a few security features available on most CBMS. Users, for example, can usually designate messages as private, meaning that they can only be accessed using an additional password. A number of systems also allow users to designate files, which contain multiple messages, as password protected.

System Administration and Maintenance

The sign-on message shows a few important features of most CBMS. First, because they are computers, they require maintenance and are also fallible. Unless the computer is completely fault-tolerant— meaning that it has a backup processor and disks waiting for the main ones to break, along with an uninterruptible power supply— it will at some point go down. In order to prevent this from happening and to perform proper system backups of files, its operators must periodically take the CBMS off service. This is usually done in the midnight hours.

The most important point here, however, is that CBMS are subject to random failures. Although the good ones have uptimes that are above 99.5 percent, Murphy's Law dictates that the one half of 1 percent outage will one day cause some pain. Unfortunately, it comes with the territory of using today's computers, but it is something that service administrators must get across to users without, of course, scaring them from using the service in the first place by blowing downtime out of proportion.

Second, the system must be managed. CBMS do not take care of themselves. Two types of management are required. The first is system management related to keeping the computer running and the files properly backed up. This management is provided by the public service provider or, typically, the MIS department when the installation is in-house. The second type is service administration, which is the responsibility of the group providing the messaging service (not always the MIS department for in-house services, and never the public service provider unless under a specific contract to provide such services at extra costs to regular usage). Service administration includes:

- Identifying applications for using the service;
- Telling users inside the company that the service exists;
- Adding and deleting users to the service;
- Training new users;
- Notifying users of important impending actions, such as the service being taken down for maintenance;
- Controlling certain group-oriented bulletin boards;
- Handling the billing;
- Registering address lists and business forms for public usage; and
- Making certain that the service is implemented properly.

Although service administration is typically not difficult, it does require a time commitment, which often adds a substantial and unexpected cost to operating a CBMS.

User Interface

When accessing any mail system, the user interacts with it through a user interface. There are three basic types of user interfaces: line oriented, screen oriented, and personal computer. In a line-oriented interface, the computer does not keep track of where the terminal's cursor is located on the screen. Thus, the computer sends information to the terminal a line at a time. In this way, the information scrolls from the top of the screen to the bottom a line at a time. When old information reaches the top of the screen, it scrolls off the top when the next line is sent and either disappears, if the user has no buffer in the terminal, or is captured so that it can be reread. Because the computer has no way of knowing where the user is located, except on a specific line, the computer presents the user with a command line called a prompt so that commands can be typed into the system.

Screen interfaces are more advanced than line interfaces. In a screen interface, the computer can keep track of the terminal's cursor. This allows the interface to divide the screen into sections, which are typically called windows. One window, for example, may contain a set of commands, whereas another may contain the inbox or a specific message that is being read.

Personal computer interfaces are designed so that users can perform most of their operations offline on the PC, using a screen interface and PC editor. These interfaces have special routines that send and retrieve messages automatically, hang up the line, and then present the new messages to their users. In CBMS with line-oriented interfaces, PC interfaces usually bear little relationship to how the online interface operates because the purpose is to improve on the appearance and operation of the online interface. In CBMS with screen-oriented interfaces, however, the PC interfaces are typically replications of the screen interface on the CBMS, although users still perform most actions offline.

In general, public CBMS services that are designed to be accessed via packet switching networks at low speeds, such as 1,200 or 2,400 bps, have line interfaces, whereas CBMS that are designed for in-house operation at speeds of 9,600 bps have both screen-oriented interfaces—when the users are accessing the system while in-house—and line-oriented interfaces—when accessing the system from remote location.

The following discussions assume that the user is accessing the CBMS via a line interface. Readers should keep in mind, however, that this type of interface is the least attractive to use. Thus, the clear trend in the field is to move to either a direct screen interface on the CBMS' host computer or to a personal computer interface.

Inbox

After successfully negotiating through the network and logging onto the CBMS, the user is typically put at a command line. Although the heart of any CBMS is its message transfer system, the head is its inbox, which keeps a list of incoming messages that have not been read. The inbox is the place where most users go first upon entering a CBMS. A few systems, in fact, automatically show users a scan of the inbox upon entering the system, although most just put the user at a command line. Figure 6-2 shows a typical inbox system scan and a command line. The *scan* command, incidentally, is almost universal and will result in a scan of the inbox.

Figure 6-2. Typical CBMS Inbox Scan

No.	Sender	Date/Time	Subject	Length
1	J.Jones	9/4/86/12:28 pm	Meeting Tomorrow	4 (Urg)
2	P.Wilson	9/4/86/9:23 am	Sales Report	36
3	D. Arnet	9/4/86/10:56 am	Comments on proposal	15 (Priv)
4	L.Barker	9/4/86/11:15 am	Re: Friday's meeting	5
5	F.Pauling	9/4/86/11:48 am	Re: Financial proposal	12
6	P.Wilson	9/4/86/12:35 pm	Question on budget	9 (Ack)
7	M.Mercer	9/4/86/1:35 pm	Re:Financial proposal	23
8	D. Arnet	9/4/86/2:22 pm	Comments on proposal	16

The scan line tells the key features about each message, including its number in the inbox, the sender, the subject, the length (in either characters or lines), the date/time of transmission, and, in some systems, the unique identifier for the message. Every system, incidentally, keeps a unique message identifier whether or not it is shown in the scan line. Although most systems allow users to find messages by searching combinations of parameters, such as all messages from J.Jones sent between April 18 and April 30, 1986, unless each message has a unique identifier, it makes it impossible to guarantee a full audit of all messages handled by the system.

System Commands

After the inbox scan, users find themselves back at the command line. Because virtually all CBMS operate with natural language commands, the CBMS is controlled much in the way that someone would give instructions to a secretary or administrative assistant. There's one hurdle, however, that most users must get over: understanding that although the CBMS tries to emulate the desktop environment, most do not have enough intelligence to function as fluidly as a person.

Perhaps the best way to view it is through another analogy. Handling a CBMS is like walking through a house. When you go into a specific room, you cannot see the other rooms and, therefore, cannot perform tasks associated with them. In the study, for example, you can take a book from the shelves or light a fire in the fireplace. You cannot, however, flop down on the bed or hop into the shower. The same is true with most CBMS. When you are in the inbox, for example, you can only perform tasks associated with messages in the inbox.

Thus, most CBMS operate on a two-step process. The first step is to choose the part of the desk where you want to operate; e.g., inbox, outbox, work space, file cabinet, directory, etc. The second step is to choose the specific operation or command. From this perspective, CBMS have two types of commands: movement and action. Movement commands take the user from one part of the system to another, whereas action commands perform tasks associated with the specific part of the CBMS.

Typical movement commands include *scan, help, directory, list, check,* and *profile*; typical action commands include *read, compose, reply, forward, send, edit, file,* and *delete*. The key movement command, incidentally, is *scan*, which not only performs the task of showing the user what is in a particular box, but also takes the user to that box so that action commands can be performed. The *help* command is also important because it provides access to the system's online documentation. To get an idea of commands available on any particular system, it's a good idea to just type *help* when first signing on. Incidentally, there usually are a few commands that are unrelated to the movement/action model. One such command is *password*, which is used to allow the user to alter his or her password. On more sophisticated systems, there is also a *change* command, which allows a series of parameters to be altered, such as the password, editor, directory listing, etc. Finally, all systems have administrative commands that are only available to the administrator(s). These commands are related to adding and deleting users, creating bulletin boards, registering business forms or address lists for public use, and other tasks that require the intervention of an administrator.

Command Syntax and Modifiers

CBMS typically have natural language commands and have a syntax like any language, although far simpler. The syntax for a CBMS command normally looks like this:

Command (modifier) (modifier)

The concept of the modifier is important because it tells the system what specific item the user wants the command to operate upon. In most cases, a modifier is required because few commands are self-standing. Modifiers, however, are often implied and do not have to be entered. For example, if the user has just scanned the inbox and wants to see the outbox, the user must specify it, as in *scan outbox*. Once the user is operating in the outbox, however, the *scan* command alone will result in the outbox being scanned. In short, most systems assume that unmodified commands operate at their present location. Movement commands typically have locations as their modifiers, such as *check notices, profile user, list files*, or *directory Jones*. In these examples, the *check* command would put the user in the bulletin board called notices; the *profile* command would show the user his or her profile on the system, which might include the type of terminal being used, the editor being used, and other changeable items; the *list* command would show a list of personal files that the user has created; and the *directory* command would show the IDs for everyone on the system named Jones.

Modifiers are what give CBMS their richness as well as their complexity. The action commands, for example, can be magnified in power significantly, allowing commands such as *read, send, file, reply, forward,* and *delete* to operate on just one message or a set of messages—depending upon the sophistication of the system. *Read 1-5*, for example, will cause the first five messages to be read in order. In this case, the system would prompt the user after each message to allow it to be replied to, forwarded, and/or filed or deleted.

Although the modifiers give CBMS their power, they are not mandatory except to designate a location or a specific message number. Users, therefore, do not have to learn long lists of modifiers to use CBMS. Most users, in fact, do little more than use single modifiers. So-called "power users", however, often know and use almost every modifier to shorten the process of handling messages.

CBMS Internal Structure

At this point, it is worthwhile to delve a bit into the internal structure of most CBMS to understand why the movement/action model is necessary. Although the CBMS may look to users like a model of their desktop and a post office delivery system, to the computer it is nothing more than a set of files that are controlled by a program. The user must direct the system to perform commands on these files. A message itself consists of a series of fields much like in a data base record. The message fields for most CBMS are shown in Figure 6-3.

Figure 6-3. Fields Within a CBMS Message

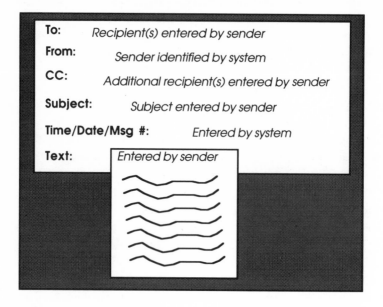

Message Handling

To save space inside the computer, messages are typically stored only once; so, each message is either a separate computer file or a record within a larger file keyed by a unique message number. Identifiers, called pointers, are stored in other files that indicate the users who have access to the messages. In this way, the user first moves to the specific box, such as an inbox, outbox, desktop, or a personal file, which is created by the user with a specific name, and then issues an action command. When a message is sent to specific recipients, for example, the computer stores the message in its specific file and then updates the inbox files of each user who has access to the message. When a recipient signs onto the system, the computer checks his or her inbox file, which contains references to the specific messages that can be read.

The action commands tell the computer to perform actions related to specific messages; e.g., show the contents of the file pointed at by the first item in the inbox (*read* command) or eliminate this reference from the work space or a personal file (*delete* command). On some CBMS, the system also performs some action commands automatically; e.g., moving a message that has been read from the inbox file to the desktop file. In this way, it is possible to move logically through the computer's storage system, performing specific actions on the messages that are pointed to in the user's different files.

Directory Structure

The CBMS directory structure is as important as its message handling structure. Without a good directory, the CBMS cannot be expanded and controlled inside of an organization. This is particularly true if the system allows alphabetic names. Many companies, for example, have people with the same or similar names. These people, however, are identified not just by their names, but by their divisions and/or departments. A good CBMS directory must make the same types of distinctions if it is to be used effectively in a corporate environment. Unfortunately, when a CBMS is chosen, the administrators will often spend more time evaluating the user interface and basic mail commands than the directory, which can be a big mistake. Most users can adjust to any interface (within limits), but the organization cannot adjust to a weak directory.

The basic issue when choosing a directory is how many levels will the directory allow. A level is the number of points in a hierarchical structure. A directory with a single level can only house individual mailboxes. A directory with a two-level structure can house individual mailboxes by department or by some other grouping. A directory with more levels may be able to track users by company, division, and department. A directory with multiple levels is particularly important for administrative issues such as billing. If the company, for example, budgets by department and bills back each department for telephone usage, travel, copying, word processing, and other administrative operations, the CBMS must be capable of handling such billing as well or it can never be accepted as a routine administrative tool.

Multilevel directories can also provide other sophisticated benefits besides billing. In such directories, it becomes possible to assign special accounts and bulletin boards that mirror the company's structure. System administration, for example, may be handled on a division or departmental level, with the administrators always having the same name but a different division or department. It is also possible to assign generic mailboxes for departmental communications so that users can send messages to the sales or personnel departments.

Multilevel directories are also important for handling business forms and distribution lists, which are typically registered by an administrator. If the directory has only one level, there can only be one form and list with the same name. Furthermore, the administrator must also update the lists and forms if changes are made. In the real world, however, forms may vary by divisions and departments, and lists will change as people take new positions. Thus, if the directory can accommodate administrators at multiple levels, it becomes far easier to distribute the administration of these important CBMS tools.

One other important benefit of a multilevel directory is automatic broadcasting at various levels in the directory's structure. In these systems, it is possible to send messages to all members of a specific branch, such as everybody in the sales department or in the automotive division.

The various mail systems on the market differ markedly in their directory structures, along with their searching capabilities; however, the majority of systems have a two-level structure so that individuals can also be identified by a single group, such as a department. There are some systems, however, such as Telemail and Envoy 100, that have an unlimited "node" structure that can fully mirror the organization's structure.

Message Integrity and Security

Because the computer just thinks of messages as files, there is no inherent message integrity or security. These must be provided as part of the CBMS program. Most CBMS have adopted a uniform set of standards related to message integrity and security, although these should be checked thoroughly during any evaluation process. The most obvious security factor is that messages can only be read by those specified in a **To** or **CC** field. This exists on all CBMS.

The better systems go one level further by providing the ability to designate certain messages as private. These messages require an additional password to be read. This allows a user to give his ID and password to a secretary or administrative assistant for routine correspondence but still receive messages that can be kept private. The problem with this type of architecture, which is quite common on CBMS, is that all of the users must know about it and also keep track of their special privacy passwords (one password is often hard enough). Many users do not know about the second level of password protection and assume that all messages on their CBMS are private, i.e., will only be read by the recipient. Thus, it is quite possible for a user who does not know about the second level of privacy to send what would be considered a confidential message without knowing that the receiver's secretary routinely retrieves all CBMS messages.

Another subtle issue is message integrity. Most CBMS have adopted the convention of not allowing a message entered into the system to be altered. Some systems, however, allow messages to be edited. Although this seems harmless enough on the surface and has benefits, such as joint document preparation, it also means that the CBMS cannot be relied upon as a system of record. If a message can be changed after it has been received, there is no way to guarantee that what is in storage has not been altered. To avoid the chance of revision but not prohibit joint document preparation, the better CBMS allow the text of messages to be placed into the editor but require that they be sent out as new messages. This guarantees message integrity.

CBMS Subsystems

For any user, the most important view of a CBMS is its functionality. From this view, a CBMS consists of a number of subsystems that perform the key functions required to emulate the way that knowledge

Figure 6-4. Functional Subsystems of Typical CBMS

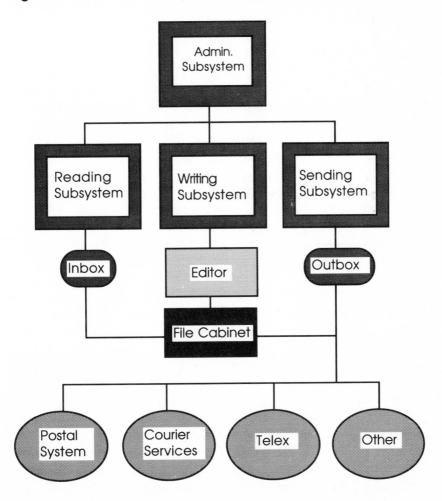

workers operate on their desktops and the way in which a postal system operates. The subsystems are Reading, Writing, Sending, and Administration, which are shown in Figure 6-4. The Administrative subsystem handles registration of users, forms, bulletin boards, and other central resources. Since Administration controls the mail system, it must be considered the leading mail subsystem. The Reading subsystem handles all the functions associated with reading and handling messages, including replying, forwarding, filing, and deleting messages. The Writing subsystem handles the creation of messages, replies, and forwarded messages and calls the system's editor when required. It interfaces with the Reading subsystem on one side and the Sending subsystem on the other. The Sending subsystem handles delivery of messages, including all the different delivery modes available on the CBMs, such as mailbox, postal delivery, courier services, telex and other modes.

Reading Subsystem

The Reading subsystem begins with the inbox and filing system. Messages from the inbox can be scanned and read typically by selecting their appropriate numbers. When each message is read, it is shown on the terminal's screen display, and/or on the local printer, if selected. The message includes the same information in its header as is shown in the scan line, along with other key information, such as the message's unique identifier. Following the message, the system will display a command line so that the user can take a number of steps associated with handling the message. Figure 6-5 shows a message as it is displayed on a typical CBMS.

Actions on Messages

Once a message is read, the user can perform four actions on the message: *reply, forward, file,* and *delete.* A key point is that more than one of these actions can be performed on the message during a *read* cycle; so, most CBMS remain focused on that message until the user issues a command to go on to another message. Most systems have a command called *next* to perform this task, although just hitting the carriage return will typically be interpreted as the default for *next.* If the user chooses *reply,* the system will put the sender's name in the **To** field of a new message and then put the user in the system's editor to write the reply. Most systems also have a *reply all* command (or some variation), which allows the reply to be sent to all members of the **To** and **CC** fields.

Figure 6-5. Typical CBMS Message

```
Command?    Read 1
From:   J.Jones    Date: Sept 4, 1986 @ 12:28 pm    Msg#135867
To:    K. Larson
       D. Arnet
       M. Mercer
CC:    P.Wilson
       T.Rutherford
Subject:    Meeting tomorrow
Text.
The meeting tomorrow will be held in the boardroom on the 3rd
floor at 3 pm. It's critical that you all attend. Our best customer,
Allied Amalgamated, will be visiting and we want to show them
the depth of our support staff management. Karl is scheduled
to give the major presentation, following which we plan to have
Bill Krause from Allied give us a presentation of their purchasing
plans for their next fiscal year. Dennis & Mike will then give a
closing presentation on our support plans for them. If there's
any last minute surprises, please let me know by phone.

—Jeff

Command?
```

Handling replies, incidentally, is one of the weaknesses of CBMS. In a human system, replies are simple because the user knows who has been sent one. In a CBMS, however, it is not clear who is sent a reply. Is it the sender? Is it the sender and everyone in the **To** field? Is it the sender and everyone in the **To** and **CC** fields? There is no universal answer. In general, however, the reply command will generate the reply only to the sender. Although most systems have modifiers that allow the reply to be extended to the message's distribution list, such as *reply!* or *reply all*, it is not clear that users know about them. It is quite possible, for example, that the majority of CBMS users could not explain how the reply command on their system works. Many, furthermore, may think that the system operates in a different manner than it actually does.

The *forward* command typically puts the user into the system's editor so that a comment can be attached to the message being forwarded and also brings up the **To**, **CC**, and **Subject** fields as well. *Forward*, however, results in the text of the original message being sent along with the comment by the new sender. The *forward* command, when used properly, can result in the equivalent of a circular memo being passed around a group of people. Although this is not efficient for generating replies rapidly, it can be used quite effectively for handling internal request/approval cycles and can be particularly powerful when combined with the business forms capabilities of the better CBMS.

The *file* and *delete* commands are opposites. In theory, one cannot file and delete a message at the same time. In practice, however, a number of CBMS require both actions to be taken if the user wishes to delete a message from the inbox while also putting it in a specific file. Most systems will also allow the same message to be stored in a number of different personal files. As the message is only stored once, it is only a small amount of overhead to store multiple pointers. On most systems, incidentally, the user gives the *file* command with a modifier specifying the name of the file, such as "file in sales_report". If "sales_report" exists, the action is carried out. If it does not exist, the system asks something like: "File does not exist. Do you wish to create it (Y/N)?" If the user answers "Y", the file will be created, and the message will be entered into it. The file "sales_report" also deserves a comment. Most computers interpret a space as the end of a character string and can only accept one string at a time. If the underline key on the terminal is used instead of a space, it allows more than one word to be entered into a single string. This subtle point is not known by most unaccustomed users, who often bend over backward trying to create files with single word names.

Modifiers

Another important part of the Reading subsystem is the command modifiers, such as *reply all, reply!,* or *read!.* There are no standards here. The more powerful systems typically distinguish themselves by their richness of modifiers. Just as the Inuit (Eskimos) may have dozens of words to delineate snow, a good CBMS may have numerous ways to read and handle messages. One powerful way is to allow time-, date-, and user-related modifiers to be combined with movement and action commands, such as *scan J.Jones since August 1* or *read! all since September 5.* This is particularly powerful if the command can cut across multiple boxes as well, although this is usually rare. Most boxes are separate subdirectories inside the computer and cannot be searched or acted upon with a single command.

Systems with these combined modifiers, but without the ability to search across personal files, can often be used with more power if the user stores all messages in a single file or just leaves them in the inbox, if possible. The *scan* command can then be used to create a view of the overall file system that is assembled based on the parameters chosen for the specific scan. Unless the system allows the scan to operate across multiple files, a single file will assure that the maximum number of messages is available for searching.

Handling Read Messages

One area where CBMS have differences is in handling messages that have been read. The weakest systems, for example, send them off into the ether unless they are filed. Most systems, however, either keep them in the inbox or place them in a separate box called the "desk" or "desktop", or the like. Both methods are acceptable. What is important, however, is how long the messages that have been read, but not filed, will be kept in the system. If the system throws them away quickly, for example, users will have to be well trained to make certain that they file messages they wish to keep. Systems that do not have any time limit are far more forgiving in this respect, but they may have their disk space filled quickly, requiring frantic requests from system administrators for users to clean up their mailboxes. This is one of the give-and-take areas of CBMS usage that has no simple set of rules. How this should be handled depends upon the applications of the CBMS and the available hardware to run them.

With the advent of sophisticated PC front end software programs, however, it is important for the administrator to have the ability to set some limit for each user on how long the messages that have been read will be retained. The reason for this is that advanced PC front end software programs will sign on automatically and retrieve all unread messages for their users, who will read the messages offline, create replies, create other messages, and keep a file of messages on the PC. The front end will then sign on again automatically and send the new messages. If the administrator cannot control the system's message retention period for each user, those who operate with advanced front end programs will end up with the system storing every message that has been read *ad infinitum*, even though the user may have long ago deleted the message from the PC's file system. This, of course, will waste system resources and, eventually, cause serious storage problems.

Checking Mailboxes

One of the most significant problems on many CBMS today is whether users check their mailboxes regularly. If a significant number of users do not check their mailboxes, then the regularity of the CBMS can be destroyed. Why send a message if there is a good chance that the user will not receive it? This problem has been largely ignored by most CBMS software vendors and public service suppliers, which means that there have been few attempts to solve the problem technically on the host. Although one might claim that proper training is the best that can be hoped for, this is not true. CBMS can have commands, such as *status*, that will tell the user whether a specific message has been read. It is also possible for a CBMS that is connected to auto-delivery devices, such as a printer, to send unread messages automatically to the printer if they are not read within a specified time; e.g., 96 hours. In this way, the CBMS can be designed to take active steps to assure that the messages are delivered to every recipient. It is also possible to use PC front end software that automatically signs on for the user at specified times to alleviate the problem.

It is difficult to overstate the importance of this issue because it can ruin the reliability of a system. Training alone, furthermore, may not solve the problem, which is related to resistance to changing habits. Although this may be impacted by training, there is little evidence that putting someone in a classroom will guarantee regular usage. For a planner, features that assure message delivery to recipients and, thus, protect the regularity and reliability of the system, should be considered strong enough to tilt the entire buying decision.

Writing Subsystem

The Writing subsystem is associated with creating messages, replies, and forwards. The main command associated with the Writing subsystem is *compose*, which has a number of synonyms, such as *create* and *send*, and which is used to initiate the message creation process on a number of systems. Its main element is the editor, which allows messages to be prepared, replied to, and forwarded with comments. There are two types of editors: line oriented and screen oriented. In general, CBMS with line-oriented interfaces will have line editors, and CBMS with screen-oriented interfaces will have screen editors.

Line Editors

Most line editors give the user a command line, which is typically different from the main command line in the CBMS. The user must then learn a series of commands to manipulate through the editor. Such commands include *read, insert, delete, move, copy, change, find*, and *format* (or some synonymous variation). To use the editor, the user must first find the appropriate line and then perform the required command, such as *delete 7, insert 5, change 6/box/boxes/*. The greatest problem is that line editors require great command precision. The command *change 6/box/boxes/* will not be accepted if the hash marks are in the wrong place or if the line number is incorrect.

Because of the wide variation in editors—and their user-unfriendliness in general—no attempt will be made to describe them in detail. To put it simply, line editors are the bane of all CBMS and should be confined as much as possible to terminals. PC users should be encouraged to switch to communication software packages that have built-in, full-screen editors. These packages are explored in more detail in the section on PCs. There is no mileage in trying to spread the use of line editors throughout an organization. The best that can be hoped for is to make them as easy to use as possible through good documentation and help files.

Screen Editors

Screen-oriented editors are far easier to use than line editors, although they too can have their problems, depending upon the CBMS. The better CBMS, for example, will use fairly sophisticated word processors as their editors. These editors have features associated with good word processors, such as wordwrap, which automatically moves a word overflowing the end of a line to the beginning of the next line, and automatic reformatting of inserted text. Some screen editors, however, may allow the user to move the cursor to any line on the screen, so that characters can be deleted or inserted, but they may not have wordwrap.

The limitations of editors, incidentally, are not always the problem of the mail system, but may be symptomatic of the computer being used. IBM mainframes, for example, do not have the ability to perform wordwrap because they only receive full screens of text. To overcome this problem, users must have a program called Entry Assist that is installed at the terminal's controller to perform wordwrapping before the screen is sent to the mainframe.

Sending Subsystem

The Sending subsystem is separate from the other subsystems—or it should be. This allows the CBMS to deliver messages to more than just mailboxes. In most organizations, for example, there are far more people without mailboxes than with them. If the Sending system is separate, it opens the doors to delivery possibilities to other networks. Public CBMS services, for example, are all connected to couriers, postal systems, and the telex network. The better in-house CBMS software packages now have these capabilities available as options. Many also connect to corporate mailrooms or communications centers (telex rooms) so that people with IDs on the CBMS can send messages to employees not on the system. In fact, one popular feature on in-house CBMS is the ability to list everyone in the organization in the directory, with those people who do not access their mailboxes having their messages automatically routed to a specific printer in the mailrooms or communications centers, and delivered as though they were paper memos or telexes.

As electronic mail grows from systems into networks, the separation of the Sending subsystem becomes more important because users will want to send messages to people on other systems. This means that any electronic mail system today should have the ability to operate in such a networked environment. If it does not, a company that must evolve from a single system into a networked environment will find itself in long-term trouble.

Envelopes

There are two parts to any message: the envelope and the text. The envelope consists of the non-text fields, including **To**, **From**, **CC**, and **Subject**. The only relationship that can be confusing is between the **To** and **CC** fields. The **CC** field is usually unnecessary on many CBMS, which make no distinction between the fields. Any action performed on the **To** field in these systems is automatically extended to the **CC** field. Its only reason for existing is because it mirrors how people operate on paper memos. There is, however, one problem that is caused by this distinction. When a user makes a reply to a message, it is not clear who receives the reply. Is it the originator of the message, everyone in the **To** and **CC** fields, or only people in the **To** field? Typically, only the sender receives a reply, although most systems have a *reply all* command that allows the reply to be sent to everyone in the address fields. Unfortunately, many users are confused by this issue and believe that they are sending replies to everyone on the list when actually the replies are only being sent to the originator.

Outbox

The outbox is often a confusing part of electronic mail systems. On some systems, it is used to house messages that have already been sent, which makes it a historical record of messages sent by the system. On other systems, the outbox houses messages that have been created but not yet sent. On a number of systems, this type of outbox is called the desk or desktop. Users must check specifically to see how the outbox on their system functions, if one is available. Interestingly, some CBMS do not use the outbox, but require the user to put his or her ID in the **To** or **CC** field to keep a copy of the message. These systems, however, will usually have an option that automatically places the sender's ID in the **CC** field of every message that he or she sends. Although it seems a mistake not to have an outbox, there is a reason why such a structure is chosen that is related to the limitations of computer files.

In a system that distinguishes inbox from outbox, it is impossible to assemble a listing of all messages related to a specific topic without putting them in a personal file. Let's take an example. If J.Jones sends a message to four people, the original will be in the outbox, which is one file in the system, and all replies will be in the inbox, which is another file. Unless Jones files the original in a personal file and then also files all the replies there, they cannot be related together. If, on the other hand, the original is placed in Jones' inbox with him as a **CC**, it is possible to assemble the original message and all of the replies by scanning the inbox. As an example, on most systems, the **Subject** field in a reply is filled out with the same words as those in the **Subject** field of the original, which has also been adopted as part of the X.400 Standard. Thus, if the user scans the inbox for the words used in the original **Subject** field, it will also identify all replies.

This does not mean, incidentally, that the outbox is a poor design concept. What it means is that CBMS, in general, have problems keeping track of group-oriented communications. Although CBMS are unparalleled in distributing messages, they can become quite confusing when used by a group to discuss a single topic over a period of time, especially as it is not certain who in the group has received replies to which messages. There are three ways to avoid this problem. The first is to set up a distribution list in the system rather than to send the message to specific members of the group and to also keep a personal file of all the communications. The second is to use a bulletin board. The third is to use a CBMS that is set up for group communications. These systems, which are called computer conferencing, are discussed in Chapter 9

Message Preparation

If the CBMS only allows mailbox deliveries, then the Sending subsystem is easy to operate. If, however, the CBMS handles offnet and networked deliveries as well, there are added complexities in knowing the proper address for each delivery mode. There are two ways to handle this. The simplest is to use modifiers to the *compose* command that specify the delivery mechanism in advance. On these systems, an unmodified *compose* command will prompt the user for the **To** and **CC** fields related to system users, whereas a modifier such as *compose telex* will result in a different prompting sequence to accept a telex address. The more complex method— but also more powerful— is to accept different types of addresses in the **To** field so that it is possible to send the same message to mailbox users on different systems in the network, telex addresses, and other offnet delivery systems. Such systems, of course, require more extensive training or very sophisticated help capabilities so that users can quickly learn the differences in address structures.

When a message is sent, most CBMS give the user a formal confirmation, such as **Message #135689 sent on Sept 5, 1986 at 11:35 pm**. This type of confirmation tells the user only that the system has sent the message. For mailbox messages, it means that the message is placed in a queue that will result in the addressees' inboxes being updated. For networked or offnet delivery messages, it means that the messages are placed in a queue to be transmitted over these gateways. The confirmation does not guarantee that the messages will be read. For a mailbox message, the addressee must take a positive action to receive the message. For a message delivered to other networks, the gateway system must deliver the message properly.

Status Checking and Sending Options

Few CBMS have the ability to check the status of every message that has been sent, although this capability is available on some and is a very powerful feature. It tells the user whether mailbox messages have been read, whether a networked message (message sent to a mail system running on another computer) or telex has been delivered, and whether an offnet message to the postal system or couriers has been printed for delivery and mailed. There are also variations of the *status* command. Some systems, for example, will only identify whether messages have been read, but they cannot tell users the results of any messages sent for delivery to other mail systems or to the telex network.

Most CBMS do not have a *status* command and will not tell the user whether a mailbox message has been delivered unless specifically requested by the sender. With telex messages, however, most CBMS will send a confirmation of delivery. With mailbox messages and other offnet messages, however, no confirmation is sent.

For mailbox messages, there are usually three or four options that are available as modifiers, such as *send urgent, send acknowledge, send registered,* and *send private.* The *urgent* and *acknowledge* options require no action by recipients other than to read the mail. The *urgent* option will cause the message to be placed at the top of the inbox list. The *acknowledge* option will cause a confirmation to be sent to the sender when the recipient reads the message. The *registered* option will typically tell the user that there is a registered piece of mail and prompt for it to be read. The *private* option will result in the recipient having to enter a separate password (not the password used upon sign-on) before being able to read the message. Although users have enough trouble remembering their regular password, the private password often causes even more problems because it is used infrequently. It is quite common for these users to forget this password and have to contact the system administrator to have it changed before being able to read the message.

Administration Subsystem

The final part of a CBMS from the user viewpoint is its Administration subsystem, which handles the user's profile, passwords, and address lists, along with the system's directory and business forms. This is often the most ignored part of the CBMS, although it is of major importance.

Profile and Passwords

The user's profile specifies what the system knows about the user. The more powerful the system, the more there will be in the profile. Most systems have very limited profiles, such as identifying the type of terminal used for access and the width of the terminal's carriage; e.g., 40 or 80 columns. The more powerful systems, however, can keep a profile of the user's preferred editor, the type of terminal, a nickname that can be used instead of the regular name, the user's preferred interface (line or screen oriented), and an auto-reply option that sends a specific message in reply to all new messages if the user is away on vacation. The user profile, incidentally, is different from the profile set up by the system administrator, who sets permissions on the system, such as commands that cannot be used, the password, and the type of group the user belongs to. It is possible, for example, to restrict who on the system the user or group can access or be accessed by. This is especially true on public services, which can keep corporations completely separate from each other, with no ability to exchange messages and no mention made in any public directory of either company's existence.

The users also control their passwords. Although they are set initially by system administrators, users can change them at will on most systems. System administrators, furthermore, cannot gain access to the password file, but they do have the ability to change the password for a user.

Address Lists

Most CBMS allow distribution lists, which is one of the most important features for group communications. Lists can be public so that all users can access them or private so that only the creator can access them. The better CBMS have ways of allowing a system administrator to take a private list and register it as a public one. Sophisticated directories, furthermore, can allow differentiation in public listings so that a user may create a list and make it available only to the department, division, company, or system.

Creating and using lists are usually quite simple. The command is either a modifier of the *compose* command, such as *compose list*, or it may be separate. The user types in the recipients' IDs in the **To** and **CC** fields and then gives the list a name. After the list is registered for use— when the name of the list is used in the **To** or **CC** fields of a regular message— it is expanded to the IDs specified in the distribution list. The purpose of lists is straightforward. They save the user the time and trouble of typing in each name every time the same group of people is sent a message.

A few of the more powerful systems also have a mailing list capability that is distinct from that of a distribution list. The mailing list is similar to a distribution list in that it houses a series of IDs, but it also has the ability to allow each message to be customized based on specific parameters in the body of the message.

Although lists are powerful, they impose a maintenance problem, especially when lists can be specified as public or private. Let's say that Jones creates a list for the Product Review Committee and has it registered as public so that everyone in the division can gain access to it. Who is responsible for maintaining the list? Is it Jones or the system's administrator? Although the administrator may be responsible for registering the list, for example, is he or she responsible for keeping it up to date? This is where the sophistication of the directory and system's administrative capabilities enter the picture. With a sophisticated structure, it is possible for the system to have multiple administrators down to the departmental level. These administrators are often the departments' main secretaries, who can be given responsibility for list maintenance and who will often know when to update lists without being asked. These secretaries, for example, are likely to know if their lists change and can be expected to change them on the system. The same administrators, incidentally, will also be responsible for maintaining business forms and adding and deleting new users.

Business Forms

Another part of the user Administrative system is business forms, which are one of the most powerful features that can be implemented on a CBMS. A business form is created by varying the system's normal prompting sequence so that users see specific prompts designed to gather information. The resulting answers are then placed in a specified place in the message so that it takes on the look of a regular form. Although many CBMS claim that they have forms capabilities, there can be a great variation. Some systems, for example, have forms languages that are a series of prompts, with no way to control the appearance of the output; others have complete forms languages that can specify the appearance of the resulting message, restrictions on acceptable answers to the prompts (field delimiters), and branching to create complex forms. Systems with screen-oriented interfaces, furthermore, can build forms that are filled out as if they were data base entry forms.

The PC has also added possibilities in this area. Because PCs are well suited to filling out forms, a few leading edge CBMS have developed subsystems designed to upload and download the forms to and from PCs, which allows records to be filled out offline on the PC and even integrated with popular PC data base management programs such as dBase III from Ashton-Tate. Other services have integrated forms with mainframe data bases. Forms that are filled out on a CBMS can be sent to the company's mainframe for data entry, and the mainframe can generate reports that are automatically sent to users on the CBMS. This allows the CBMS to be used for order entry or for applications such as automatically generating customized price lists.

Forms should be considered a very powerful CBMS feature, especially in the context of electronic mail as a strategic technology. One of the best applications of electronic mail is to convert a form that suffers from delays in physical delivery to online delivery. To give one example, Telecom Canada has set up a form on its electronic mail service, Envoy 100, that can be used by the Federal Government to order telecommunications services. Requests for telecommunications services are initiated in a government department and are sent on a form to the telecommunications department, which denies or approves the request and then handles placing the order. Such forms can sit on managers' desks for one or two weeks during the cycle. By using a special form on Envoy 100, managers can cut a week or two off the ordering cycle. This improves response time for government departments, and it means additional hard dollars to Telecom Canada, which can fill orders one or two weeks faster than if paper forms were used. If the order is for a private line leased at a rate of $1,000 per month, for example, Telecom Canada makes $250 for every week cut off the ordering cycle. If planners look carefully, they can often find many of these situations inside their own organizations.

Forms is also an area where mail system developers can add major enhancements, such as the ability to track the form on its route throughout the organization. In this way, everyone with the need to know can pinpoint where the form resides and help speed it along, if necessary. Another potential enhancement would be to create separate records of purchasing requests or other forms that have financial implications for the company. The record might capture the amount of the transaction, the date the money would be required, and the department where the request was originated. Such a record might then be sent to the finance department where it could be consolidated with other requests. The benefit would be a new type of financial tracking system that identified the requests in progress for either capital purchases or expenses. Needless to say, such a system would be of substantial interest to people inside organizations who monitor the company's cash flow and dispensation of its budgets. Such a system, however, would only be valuable if every form in the company were sent in via the electronic mail network.

Directory

Earlier in this section, the importance of the directory was discussed from the viewpoint of its structure. From the user's viewpoint, of course, the most important issue is that the directory be easy to access and use. Most CBMS have a directory command that operates with modifiers, such as *directory "Jones"*. Most systems, incidentally, require that the name be placed in quotations in order for a search to be carried out on all users with a similar name. Otherwise, the directory will search for an exact match of an ID. Thus, *directory "Jones"* will result in all people with Jones as part of their ID being listed, such as JJones, MJones, and LJones, whereas *directory Jones* will cause the directory to search for someone with the specific ID Jones. If it is not found, the directory will say something like **User ID not found**. This is important because many users do not know this subtle distinction and often find the directory useless because they do not use the quotation marks. This is something to be stressed during training.

Networked Directories

The directory problem becomes especially important when electronic mail evolves from a system to a network. Most electronic mail systems, for example, have the ability to be networked with sister mail systems from the same vendor operating on other computers. Unless the network is set up so that the directories from each system can be accessed across the network, however, users will have to send messages to other systems without knowing if the users have valid IDs. They will also not be able to search other directories for users.

In general, the basic technique employed by most vendors for networking directories is to have the complete directory of users in the entire network duplicated on each system. In such a structure, every change to a specific directory is automatically sent to every system in the network so that the directories remain in sync. This networked directory strategy works well when the number of nodes is small, such as in the 5- to 20-node range. When the number of nodes becomes larger, however, directory update traffic begins to become a major overhead item on the network. To give one example, Digital Equipment estimates that when it reached the 200-node range, more than 90 percent of all network traffic was related to directory updates. The issue of networked directories is explored in more detail in Chapter 12 on Corporate Mail Networks.

Summary

Computer-based message systems often seem simple on the surface but have many complexities when they are studied in detail. Available systems also look very similar, especially when users only compare the features in a Yes/No type of checklist. In practice, however, CBMS are quite different in how they implement many of the features, so that all features are not equal. An ability to assure that recipients receive their messages, for example, is uncommon; yet this feature might be lost in a Yes/No checklist, even though it can be more important than all the other features combined if there is a problem with users checking their inboxes regularly. The CBMS that have similar Reading, Writing, and Sending subsystems, furthermore, also can differ markedly in their Administrative subsystems. Planners must carefully identify their major applications and then take all the subsystems into consideration before choosing the right CBMS for them. This is especially true of the Administrative subsystem, which should be viewed with the long-term evolution of the service in mind. The system that appears to be the best for initial applications may turn out to be one of the worst from the perspective of spreading usage throughout the organization.

CBMS Services and Systems

CBMS are available as either public services or private systems. Although the public services are better known because of the marketing efforts of their vendors, there are more users in North America on private systems operated in-house. There are also considerably more messages sent on in-house systems than on public services. This section explores public services and private systems on the market.

Public Services vs. Private Systems

One of the first questions that any company addresses is whether to use a public service or operate a private system. Both have advantages and disadvantages. The main advantages to a public service are:

- High reliability;
- Access to offnet delivery capabilities such as telex, next-day courier delivery, and two-day postal service delivery;
- Widespread availability via nationwide packet networks;
- The ability to communicate with users from other companies; and
- The availability of public bulletin boards and data bases (on many, but not all, of the public services).

The major disadvantages of public services are:

- The cost per user;
- Relatively weak file transfer capabilities; and
- The requirement that users operate with line editors while online.

The major advantages of most private systems are:

- Low access cost per user;
- Availability of full-screen editors;
- Ability to network inside the company;
- Relatively good file transfer capabilities; and

• The ability to integrate with other internal applications.

The major disadvantages are:

• Reliability;
• Requirement of good technical personnel to support the system; and
• The inability to connect to people outside the company.

Choosing a Public Service or a Private System

Choosing whether to use a public service or private system is situational. Companies that want to offer their users integrated office systems with word processing, calendars, financial planning, and data base access, along with electronic mail will almost certainly opt for a private system. For companies that want just a mail system, the choice is more difficult. In general, the decision point should be based upon the location of the users. The more geographically dispersed the users, the more the company should consider opting for a public service. In terms of company size, there is no hard-and-fast crossover point where a private system is less costly than a public service. As an example, there are companies with five users that operate on a private system, and there are also a few organizations with upward of 10,000 users that operate on a public service.

A common strategy for many companies is to begin trials using electronic mail on a public service. After the need for mail is well proven and the user base is growing, the company should then consider investing in its own system. Because companies are very diverse in their policies, however, the decision is based on personal, as well as, economic reasons. There are some companies, for example, that require that all computer services, including electronic mail, be provided on in-house systems, regardless of expense. These firms like to have total control over where important information resides. These companies will typically purchase electronic mail software that runs on their corporate mainframes. There are other companies that prefer to have their electronic mail system run on a public service to avoid the need to purchase hardware and be responsible for its operation. These companies may have 10,000 or more users operating on a public service, even though the cost is substantially higher than if they operated their own in-house service. These companies believe that the increased reliability and direct availability of offnet capabilities is worth the additional costs. In short, the choice of a public service versus a private system depends as much on the company's style as on any hard dollar economic analysis of costs.

Public Service to Private System Gateways

When public services were first introduced, their vendors made considerable efforts to convince companies not to invest in their own private systems but to use the public service instead. Today, most public services take a very different approach, encouraging companies to interlink their private systems via gateways. The public services make a strong argument that their capabilities complement any private system by allowing users direct access to telex, next-day courier delivery, two-day postal delivery, and users from other companies operating on the public service. In fact, using a gateway connection to a public service is a good way to communicate to key customers and suppliers without giving them access to an in-house system. For this reason, the public service versus private system debate is beginning to melt away. Basically, every company with electronic mail has a good reason to use a public service either directly for all messaging needs or indirectly via a gateway for offnet delivery and access to users in other companies.

Offnet Delivery Capabilities

One of the major advantages of public services is the ability to interconnect to other mail and message delivery networks, such as telex, courier services, and the postal system. To date, however, these capabilities have not lived up to their potential because of operational problems. When the public services first introduced delivery via courier and postal services, for example, they were not well integrated with PCs. Users typically had to write their letter on a word processor, translate from the word processor's format to ASCII (making sure that hard carriage returns were inserted in every line), exit the word processor and load up the telecommunications package, log-on to the mail system, transmit the ASCII file, and then reread it to make sure that no errors occurred during transmission. To add insult to injury, the offnet printers had their own pagination schemes; thus, users could never be certain where page breaks would be made unless they spent more time online using cumbersome page preview options that displayed text line by line. In short, next-day courier and postal service delivery capabilities were often harder to use than just printing the document locally and handing it to a courier or using facsimile.

Public services are now making major strides in their next-day delivery capabilities. MCI Mail, for example, has introduced a service that allows PC users to send formatted files directly to Apple Laser-Writer printers at the company's four printing locations so that files can be printed with integrated text and graphics exactly as they would appear as if printed locally. The Apple LaserWriter can handle any file that produces Postscript output, which is supported by both Apple and IBM as their standard page description language for desktop publishing. Although Macintosh computer programs are already Postscript compatible, most IBM PC applications are also adding Postscript capability. Word processors and communication packages are also more intelligent; so, it is easier to create the proper files and to handle the electronic delivery. Such capabilities are reversing the earlier problems involved with sending electronic mail for printing and delivery; it is now as easy to send a file to many of the public services for printing and next-day or two-day delivery as it is to use a courier service.

The public services have also made major strides in telex capabilities. When public services initially implemented telex connections, they were via gateways that allowed users to send telexes easily enough using store-and-forward techniques but not to receive return telexes. Today, most of the public mail services issue their users valid telex numbers that appear to the recipients as if the telexes came from a regular telex machine. Some of the services, such as Telenet and RCA Mail, have introduced the ability to access telex machines in real-time; thus, CBMS users can replace their telex machines completely. This opens up the full base of more than 2 million telex machines worldwide to most public CBMS users.

During the next few years, the public services will improve their existing telex and offnet printing services and will also add facsimile machines to the network so that users will be able to direct messages to the huge base of facsimile devices developing worldwide. This will especially benefit users with desktop publishing and other graphics applications.

The Question of Privacy

One of the main reasons why some companies have shied away from public services or private mail systems concerns privacy. In late 1986, the U.S. Congress passed the *Communications Privacy Act of 1986*, which gave official privacy status to both public and private electronic mail systems. It is now a crime to attempt to enter any electronic mail system illegally. Electronic mail records are also covered by the same wire-tapping and subpoena laws that govern other communication services such as the telephone. Both existing mail system records and backup tapes are covered by the law so that police authorities cannot request a search of records without first showing probable cause. Users must also be notified in the event that any police agency does request records. The U.S. actions to protect the privacy of electronic mail usage are a first worldwide; so, they will certainly serve as a model for many other countries that are now dealing with the same issues.

Public CBMS Services

There are now about 50 companies in North America offering public CBMS services of varying sizes and shapes, including telecommunications companies whose electronic mail services are part of a vertical series of products, timesharing companies that allow their users to send electronic mail as an adjunct to other services, and small startup firms that offer specialized services. As this is a book on planning for electronic mail, not a market research study of CBMS vendors, no attempt is made to identify every vendor or even the majority of vendors. The purpose is to identify the types, features, and pricing policies of public services offered in the market. Planners should keep in mind that their needs may be served as well or even better by a smaller vendor not identified in this book. Furthermore, as there is a lead time from when this book is being written to when it is published, there will almost certainly be new services entering the market as well as enhancements to existing services.

Planners should also keep in mind that it is easy for a small vendor to become national or even international in reach because of public packet switching networks. All it takes to open the doors to international access is to put the host up on a public network. This makes it easy for a company with advanced host services to establish a roadway that can be accessed by users worldwide.

There are 13 companies in North America whose CBMS services are covered here. These firms, of course, are not all the same size nor do they have the same market shares. In Canada, Telecom Canada's Envoy 100 is by far the largest in the market, with a share of 90 percent of all users. In the United States, Western Union's Easylink is the largest service, although there is no clear market leader as in Canada. Easylink has an estimated 25- to 30-percent share of the market.

There is also a trend in the market for specialized resellers that repackage a public CBMS service to meet the needs of a vertical industry or interest group. These resellers often bundle an electronic mail service with data base services and PC-based front end software. Because the resellers focus within one industry, they are often in a better position then the larger vendors to provide high quality service to that industry.

The firms covered in this book are:

Company	Service	City
AT&T	AT&T Mail	Basking Ridge, N.J.
BT Dialcom	Dialcom	Silver Spring, Md.
CNCP Telecommunications	Dialcom	Toronto, Ont.
CompuServe	Infoplex	Columbus, O.
Computer Sciences	Notice	El Segundo, Calif.
GE Info Services (Geisco)	Quik-Comm	Rockville, Md.
Graphnet	Freedom Network	Teaneck, N.J.
Incomnet	PeopleNet	Westlake Vill., CA
McDonnell-Douglas	OnTyme II	Cupertino, Calif.
MCI	MCI Mail	Washington, D.C.
Telecom Canada	Envoy 100	Ottawa, Ont.
Telenet	Telemail	Reston, Va.
Western Union	Easylink	Saddle River, N.J.

Comparing Public Services

Comparing public CBMS is a difficult task. It is possible, for example, to develop a comparison chart using Yes/No techniques for the availability of various features. Such a chart, however, would turn out to be virtually useless for a planner, except as a checkpoint. The reason is that the existence of equivalent features does not mean that each service implements them to the same degree, prices them identically or focuses their marketing efforts on them. Most of the services on the above list, for example, would look identical based on a list of major features, including mailboxes, offnet delivery capabilities, business forms, upload and download, directories, bulletin boards, and billing capabilities. In reality, however, they are far from identical. Instead, each service has developed its own characteristics and special capabilities that distinguish it in the market.

To give one example, both MCI Mail and Telemail have offnet delivery services that feature telex, postal service, and courier delivery options. MCI Mail, however, allows Postscript-compatible files to be printed out on Apple LaserWriters exactly as delivered, which allows integrated text/graphics documents to be submitted to the printing subsystem. Telemail's printing service can only handle ASCII files. In contrast, Telemail gives users a standard telex number and has features such as real-time telex connection, whereas MCI Mail's telex service only has store-and-forward delivery capability. Users also receive a telex number with a special prefix, which makes it harder for the recipient to send a return telex. Naturally enough, if telex is an important feature, users will tilt toward Telemail. If sending Postscript files is more important, the user will opt for MCI Mail.

Pricing

Comparing pricing is a problem in electronic mail services, which all have different pricing schemes. In general, there are two types of schemes that are used: time oriented and transaction oriented. A time-oriented service makes charges based on the amount of time that a user is online, whereas a transaction-oriented service makes charges based on the number of messages that are sent and/or received. A number of services also have pricing that is based on some combination of time and transactions. As an example, several vendors make charges based on the time that a user is online, the number of characters transmitted in messages, and the number of recipients.

In order to compare prices directly, a user must first create a usage model that takes into consideration all of the separate parameters used by the various vendors. The model must consider the number of messages being transmitted, their length, the length of time spent online to send the letters, the length of time spent online to read the messages, and the number of recipients of each message. When such a model is created, it is possible to map each vendor's pricing scheme into the model to determine comparative prices.

In the September 1984 issue of *EMMS*, I performed such a pricing comparison based upon a single user. Based upon factors such as whether PC front ends were used to keep users offline as much as possible, rates varied from as low as $25 per month to more than $100. Thus, different public services can have a wide price range depending upon the application. It is literally impossible, however, to say that one vendor is less costly than another, except in reference to a specific application, i.e., a specific model of usage. For this reason, no attempt is made in this book to compare pricing for the different public services. Users must create their own usage models and then compare pricing on an application-by-application basis. Users should also keep in mind that the vendor with the lowest price may not be the one that best meets a user's needs. Although most of the services have similar features on a Yes/No checklist, they are not implemented in the same way. Thus, the only way to determine which vendor is the best is in reference to a specific application.

AT&T Mail

AT&T is a relative newcomer to the CBMS market, entering in 1986. AT&T Mail's strengths are its offnet delivery capabilities via a network of laser printers, interconnection to domestic and international telex networks, and its integration with PCs. AT&T sells telecom packages for the IBM PC and Apple Macintosh, for example, that allow almost seamless integration. Mail can be text messages or PC files and is transferred in batch mode to the host system so that the user prepares and reads messages while offline. When using these packages, all mail is transferred using the Xmodem file transfer protocol, which eliminates transmission errors.

Pricing for AT&T Mail is based on transactions, with fixed rates for each piece of mail transmitted based on message units. As AT&T developed the system primarily for PCs, it distinguishes between messages created offline versus those created using the online editor, for which it has a fee.

AT&T Mail is the second shot in AT&T's major move into the electronic mail market. AT&T's first shot was entry into the facsimile industry in 1984. AT&T Mail itself is part of a strategy to have a central distribution service for mail flowing from in-house private systems. AT&T's in-house mail package for UNIX is called Private Message Exchange (PMX), which is an attempt to make an analogy between public telephone central office switches and PBXs.

BT Dialcom

Dialcom was one of the earliest CBMS on the market and is now one of the most mature. Dialcom was started to provide timesharing services to the Federal Government and found its first need for mail from this user base. Dialcom's major strengths are its integration with data bases and its international networking capability. Dialcom's early management adopted a strategy of following the telex tracks around the world to license its service to Postal, Telephone and Telegraph authorities (PTTs) or private licensees, with each CBMS networked together. Today, Dialcom has more than 15 licensees worldwide, which makes it an ideal service for a company with offices in several countries. Instead of the company having users make international packet network calls, which cost about $15 per hour, users can make a local call to the Dialcom licensee in each country and have messages transferred between systems at $1.00 for the first 1,000 characters and 50¢ for each additional 1,000. Using the networking capability is also simple. Each licensee has a system number so that addressing a message in the **To** field to 05:MSG257, for example, would send the message to the user with ID MSG257 on system 05 (in this case, Israel).

Dialcom has a number of major news-oriented data bases on its service and can also handle private data bases from its clients. Dialcom also allows users to gateway from its host to external data bases. In addition, Dialcom has a special Electronic Publishing (E-PUB) service that gives its users menu capabilities so that they can select the various services from menus. The data bases, furthermore, can be searched automatically via key words, with any match placed in the user's mailbox as a message. As an example, public relations departments can have news wires searched for stories about companies or competitors, with any story placed in their mailbox as a message.

Dialcom has also not forgotten PCs via its File Transfer (FT) service that allows full upload and download of files. FT, however, is a separate module from mail and is not integrated with the user's basic inbox. An ASCII, text, or expanded hexidecimal file sent to FT must be transferred manually to the mail system before it can be sent to another user. Dialcom also has a specialized PC software package, called UpFront, that provides a customized interface for PC users.

Pricing for Dialcom is based on online time, with a variety of rates based upon the different applications being used. The mail service is part of Dialcom's basic rate, which includes access to certain data bases as well.

Dialcom itself has gone through a number of management changes. In 1982, it was purchased from its original management by ITT, which sold it to British Telecom in 1986. British Telecom has made a major commitment to Dialcom on a worldwide level and has made a major investment in converting its software to X.400 compatibility. Dialcom, in fact, is now a public Administrative Domain for X.400 message traffic.

CNCP Telecommunications

CNCP Telecommunications operates its own packet switching network and is the sole provider of domestic telex service in Canada. Its CBMS is licensed from BT Dialcom. In the past, CNCP has been restricted from offering data base services because of Canadian regulations; as a result its service has been a pale shadow of the one offered by Dialcomin the United States. Recent regulatory changes, however, have opened the door to CNCP offering data base-oriented services that have distinguished Dialcom in the U.S. market. Pricing for CNCP is time oriented.

CompuServe's Infoplex

CompuServe was one of the first companies to provide public CBMS for corporate users, although its mail service has been eclipsed in name by its consumer-oriented CompuServe Information Service. Infoplex, however, continues to be well received by corporate users and boasts more than 130 customers. CompuServe is now focusing on providing Infoplex as part of a general data base/communications service to corporate customers. The data base service was developed initially for its consumer service, but is now being reoriented for commercial usage. Pricing for Infoplex is based upon the number of commands that are used, which is related to the number of messages created, sent, and stored.

Computer Sciences' Notice

Notice is an example of a general CBMS that has evolved into a system that specializes in CBMS to data base connections. The service itself was originated for use by Computer Sciences Corp.'s (CSC) timesharing customer base, but has turned into a vehicle for adding new timesharing customers via its special business forms features. A business form, for example, can be sent to a mainframe data base, which opens the door to data collection, order entry, automated price distribution, and other specialized applications.

Notice operates on CSC's Infonet packet switching network and can be accessed via IBM 3270 terminals as well as by ASCII terminals. CSC also has specialized PC software designed to automate interaction with the service and to handle file transfers. The PC package is designed especially for companies sending messages internationally and allows messages to be consolidated on the PC during the day and sent over the network at night at reduced rates.

Pricing for Notice is based on the time that the user is on the system, along with the number of characters that are transmitted.

Geisco's Quik-Comm

Quik-Comm began in the 1970s as a message system for use by General Electric Information Service's (Geisco) timesharing customers and was used primarily as a means of transmitting messages internationally as a low priced alternative to telex. Today, Quik-Comm is still used primarily by Geisco's timesharing customers, although the company is reaching out to expand its user base and is also expanding its efforts to link in-house mail systems with its public mail service via gateways. As an example, Chrysler uses a gateway from Quik-Comm to allow its automobile dealers and remote sales force to communicate to people on its IBM-based PROFs in-house system.

Quik-Comm is a general mail service aimed initially at multinational corporate users. Half of its 250-plus customers, for example, use the system for international message transmission. In the past two years, however, Geisco has targeted electronic mail as a major strategic service. To beef up Quik-Comm, Geisco has introduced a customized PC software package designed to allow file transfers and offline message creation. Geisco has a bulletin board service that is aimed at group communications; it also offers telex access, an offnet paper delivery mechanism that puts letters in the U.S. Postal Service, and the ability to send messages, such as data for entry to a data base, to other time-sharing applications running on Geisco's system.

Geisco has also become one of the leaders in shifting pricing from a time orientation to transactions. Geisco charges for sending messages based upon their size. Pricing also reflects the amount of use of the bulletin board, sending PC files, and using the system's online editor.

Graphnet's Freedom Network

Graphnet is one of the oldest value-added carriers in the United States, setting up operations to provide value-added messaging services in competition with Western Union in 1974. Today, Graphnet has one of the largest message communication networks, the Freedom Network, which allows a wide variety of terminal types, PCs, and office automation systems to exchange information at speeds up to 1,200 bps.

The Freedom Network, which has more than 5,000 customers, has services that include direct device-to-device connections, mailboxing, store-and-forward, and offnet postal service connections. Its offnet USAM (United States Automated Mail) service is particularly innovative and allows customers to send their messages with full-color logos and electronic signatures. Customers may also include business reply envelopes with the mail. Pricing has elements of both time and transactions, depending upon the type of message being transmitted.

Incomnet's PeopleNet

Incomnet is a small company whose service is discussed here because of its relative uniqueness in the market. Unlike the other CBMS, for example, PeopleNet is designed exclusively for PCs, with a major focus on direct file transfer. The service uses a message switching system at its center and has front end controllers available for users who want to have information come directly to their PCs. The front end controllers are connected directly to the PCs and must also be connected directly to the telephone network or to a packet network, so that it can be reached directly by the central switch.

PeopleNet users all have a specialized PC software package that is used to read and create messages, which can be either ASCII text or attached formatted, or binary, files. When messages are created, they are sent to the front end controller, which handles all interaction with the switching network independent of the PC. This means that messages can be sent or received while users are working on other programs or when the computers are turned off.

PeopleNet is an example of a specialized service that is not designed to compete against the mainstream electronic mail services in the marketplace. While it has mailbox capability, its main focus is on forced delivery of messages. To obtain this capability, these users pay a premium of up to $800 for a front end controller and also must have a dedicated telephone line or dedicated Direct-Inward-Dial (DID) extension on a PBX. PeopleNet also has the ability to have messages sent via satellite for wide area broadcast networks.

McDonnell-Douglas' OnTyme II

Along with Telenet's Telemail, OnTyme was one of the earliest entrants into the market and for similar reasons. Telenet and McDonnell-Douglas operate the two largest public packet networks in North America and electronic mail was seen by both companies as a natural service for these networks. OnTyme II's features match the basic online mail capabilities of most public services, with the special capability of linking its business forms directly into its time-shared data base services, which has been a major marketing focus for the firm during the past few years. As an example, it has a number of customers who use electronic mail almost transparently as the vehicle to transport information to and from its data bases. OnTyme II, however, does not have the extensive set of offnet capabilities offered by most of its competitors, nor is it focusing efforts on gateways to in-house mail systems. OnTyme II's pricing is a mix of time and characters transmitted.

MCI Mail

MCI became a sensational entrant into electronic mail in 1983 when it introduced itself as the Nation's New Post Office via television advertising, which was a first for the industry. It also cut a deal that gave each Dow Jones subscriber an automatic MCI Mail ID as well as giving each MCI Mail subscriber access to Dow Jones' data base. As a result it started life with 80,000 mailboxes, although most Dow Jones users did not know it at the time. MCI also was the first company to adopt transaction pricing and to focus on offnet delivery via the USPS and courier services. Since its introduction, MCI Mail has also added features such as bulletin boards, telex interconnection, and business forms via uploading and downloading dBase files. MCI Mail has its Link program for interconnection with private electronic mail systems; it also has sophisticated PC front end software packages developed for both IBM PC and Apple Macintosh computers as part of joint ventures with Lotus Corp. and Apple.

The Lotus Express package is a full version of MCI's Link protocol that allows private systems to gateway to MCI Mail. It allows IBM PC users to interact with MCI Mail almost entirely offline. Apple's Desktop Express implements MCI Mail in an icon/mouse environment, making it one of the easiest mail packages to use. Both allow users to send formatted files through the system as long as recipients have the same package. They also allow files output with the Postscript page description language to be printed for courier or post office delivery on Apple LaserWriters that have been installed in MCI's four printing locations in the United States.

Although most of the other public services have focused on corporate users, MCI focused initially on individual users. In 1985, however, MCI introduced its MCI Mail Link program and has also stepped up its corporate user program.

MCI Mail's transaction-oriented pricing has become a model for other companies in the industry. AT&T Mail, for example, has virtually copied MCI Mail, but with slightly lower rates. The pricing is based on the size of the message being sent and the manner of delivery.

Telecom Canada's Envoy 100

Envoy 100 is the leading CBMS in Canada by a substantial margin. The service is offered nationwide by Telecom Canada, an organization formed by all the major telephone companies in Canada to develop cross-company services. Envoy 100 itself is licensed from Telenet and has all of Telemail's basic features. In addition, Envoy is interconnected to Canada Post and features the lowest cost next-day letter delivery system in North America. Although most next-day delivery systems use couriers and are priced in the $7 to $8 range, EnvoyPost delivers letters for in the $2 to $4 range, depending upon their size.

Envoy 100 has become the messaging system of Canada and is used by both individual subscribers and by corporations. Although Telecom Canada initially focused heavily on its forms capability to enlist corporate clients, it now also emphasizes its ability to be used as an intercompany message delivery system and is one of the few firms to have published a paper directory of its subscribers. It is also internetworked to Telemail in the United States and to other Telemail licensees and to private mail systems via X.400 gateways.

Envoy's pricing plan is based on the number of characters entered into the system and of addressees to whom the messages are sent.

Telecom Canada itself does not sell PC front end software. Envoy 100's popularity has driven out a number of packages from third-party software houses, which make it easier for PC users to use Envoy 100.

Telenet's Telemail

Telemail was launched by Telenet in 1979 and has become one of the leaders in corporate usage. Recently, it introduced individual user subscriptions for $20 per month plus usage. Telemail offers a full complement of features, including basic mailbox service, bulletin boards, a sophisticated forms creation capability, and offnet and auto-delivery services. Telemail also has a sophisticated PC front end software, called PCTelemail, that makes the service easy to use and also allows formatted or binary PC files to be transferred via the system to other PCTelemail users. Telemail's basic marketing thrust is toward corporate users, with its major focus on generic messaging and its business forms capability. The forms, however, cannot be linked into mainframe data bases. Instead, they are used to replace the flow of paper forms inside organizations.

Telemail remains one of the companies that has not yet switched to transaction pricing. Its rates are based primarily on hourly usage, although it also charges for transmitted characters and additional addressees.

Telemail is also one of the leaders in the market for telex interconnection, offering such capabilities as both store-and-forward and real-time interconnection. Users receive an internationally standard telex number and are charged lower rates than those charged by international record carriers, such as ITT Worldcom, because telex traffic is carried by its CCI International telex refiling subsidiary. Telenet recently announced the ability to deliver business letters by courier or postal service, with a feature that allows users to print their letterheads and signatures.

Telenet is a major player in the electronic mail industry on a worldwide basis and its strategy is to license Telemail in other countries. To date, there are more than 15 licensees. To interconnect its licensees worldwide, Telenet has already implemented a gateway for X.400 mail systems and provides interconnection services to private X.400 systems as well.

Western Union's Easylink

Easylink is the leading CBMS service in North America, with an estimated 30 percent of the market. Easylink gets its strength from Western Union's base of telex subscribers, many of whom have switched from the telex network to Easylink. The service itself, interestingly, has one of the weaker user interface on the market and looks more like an old-fashioned telex store-and-forward system than a CBMS. Easylink also does not have an online editor as do other CBMS.

What has made Easylink successful for PC users, however, is an IBM PC front end software package, the Instant Mail Manager, that was the first custom PC front end package on the market for a public electronic mail service. The Instant Mail Manager has a built-in editor and is designed so that messages can be created offline or on the PC while the user is online. Recently, Western Union added what it calls the Instant Forms Manager to allow users to create business forms that can be filled out offline and transmitted via Easylink.

Easylink itself is designed to interconnect all its services so that users with telex machines, ASCII terminals, and PCs can interact on one network. Mailbox messages can be transferred to any Easylink user regardless of terminal type. All users have access to the telex network and Mailgram, which is connected to the USPS for next-day letter delivery, as well as to a computer letter service. Easylink also allows access to a variety of data bases, such as its FYI news service, the Official Airlines Guide, and Infocom, a unique service that allows users to access more than 1,000 separate data bases in North America using artificial intelligence searching techniques. When using Infocom, the user specifies the information that is sought, and the service determines in which data bases to search for the information. Easylink is the first major CBMS service in North America to implement and gateway to the facsimile network.

Western Union views Easylink as a public system that can be used by individuals, corporations, and in-house messaging users. Like MCI, Western Union has software that allows users on in-house systems to access Easylink for both mailbox and telex delivery. Western Union also has the largest sales force in the industry dedicated to selling its service, which gives it the greatest exposure to corporations in terms of direct contact with purchasers.

Summary

As can be seen from the description of the various services, they are all similar, yet different. The major differences are generally in pricing policies, availability of data bases, and the ability to integrate with mainframe data bases. The services also operate differently, although all of them are about equally easy to learn and to use, especially if the user is operating with a sophisticated PC-based front end package.

Evolution of Public Services

Public electronic mail services have gone through one development phase and are now in their second phase. The first phase saw the development of basic mailbox services, along with rudimentary business forms subsystems and interconnection to other message delivery services, such as telex, postal systems, and couriers. A few vendors also forged connections to data base systems and between their services and in-house message systems.

The second phase of development, which is already underway, will see improved integration with PCs, implementation of the X.400 public messaging standard, development of improved bulletin board and conferencing capabilities, increased integration with data bases, more links with in-house systems, and integration with facsimile machines. It will likely be five years before all these features are implemented across the base of public message services. When the phase is completed, however, interacting with a public mail service will have little resemblance to interacting with today's systems. Because of sophisticated PC front end software, most direct interaction, for example, will be to read messages on bulletin boards and conferencing systems or to retrieve information from data bases, rather than to create, send, and read basic mail messages and formatted files.

During this period, there will be a strong trend toward private organizations operating their own internal mail systems so that many people who now use public mail networks directly will instruct their local mail node to send the message instead. This will give the public mail services a very different flavor. Their direct user bases will increasingly migrate from large and medium-sized corporations to small businesses, individuals, user groups, and customer service departments from vendor organizations, while their indirect bases will grow from gateways to private systems. Numerous trade associations will link their members on public electronic mail services. Companies will also set up public customer service networks on public services to communicate with the growing base of online subscribers. These trends are already visible in the market and will became far more prevalent as these networks become easier to use.

Private CBMS Systems

Although public CBMS services are the best known in the market, there are far more users on systems operated inside their companies. Already there are an estimated 3 to 5 million users on private CBMS systems, with growth at a staggering rate of about 50 percent per year. There is little indication that growth will decline. In fact, the growth will likely continue throughout the decade.

Private electronic mail systems are dominated by the leading computer and communication companies, including IBM, Digital Equipment, Data General, Hewlett-Packard, Unisys, Wang, Northern Telecom, and AT&T. In addition to these firms, there are literally dozens of companies that offer electronic mail packages for in-house operation. LANs are also attracting electronic mail suppliers, with numerous products reaching the market.

The number of electronic mail packages is now so great that it is beyond the scope of this book to describe every one. It is possible, however, to describe some of the leading packages to indicate the types of features that are available on in-house mail systems. Although some of these packages are very similar to public service software, in general, the in-house mail packages tend to have more integration with word processors, other office automation tools, and PCs. In fact, many of the leading packages are designed as part of integrated office systems.

The in-house systems also tend to have screen-oriented interfaces, whereas the public services have line-oriented interfaces. The reason is that most in-house systems are used via direct connections at speeds up to 9,600 bps, whereas most public services are used at 1,200 or 2,400 bps via modems and connections over packet networks. This, of course, makes the in-house systems easier to learn and to use. In-house systems have another interesting difference. Although the public services have developed PC front end programs that operate with entirely different interfaces than do the host-based mail services, the in-house systems have developed PC front end programs and interfaces that are almost identical to the host-based services. In this way, users operating offline on a PC have the same command structure as users operating online.

The products covered in this book are:

Company	Product	City
Applied Data Research	ADR/eMail	Princeton, N.J.
Data General	CEO	Westboro, Mass.

Digital Equipment Corp.	ALL-IN-1	Merrimack, N.H.
Hewlett-Packard	HPDeskmanager	Palo Alto, Calif.
IBM	PROFs	Armonk, N.Y.
Verimation	MEMO	Rockleigh, N.J.
PCC Systems	cc:Mail	Palo Alto, Calif.

Comparing Private Systems

Readers should keep in mind that the above products are far from the only ones that can meet their needs. These have been selected to illustrate the features of private electronic mail systems.

Applied Data Research's ADR/eMail

ADR's electronic mail package, ADR/eMail, runs on IBM mainframes under the MVS, DOS, or OS operating systems and requires either IBM's CICS or ADR's ROSCOE teleprocessing monitors. Like many of the in-house electronic mail products, far more is offered than basic mailbox message communications. ADR/eMail has a built-in calendar, eDate, that allows users to schedule and track activities. Messages can be directed to other computer applications as well as to user mailboxes. Individuals can also transfer ASCII PC files and use their own PC editor using ADR's PC/eMail package.

ADR/eMail has two different operation modes. Infrequent users can interact with a menu for major functions, which eases the use of the system, whereas frequent users can interact in a command mode. The system provides basic mailbox functions such as *send, receive, forward, reply to, file,* and *delete.* Users can create an unlimited number of folders and can also have messages archived for later offline retrieval. One significant design feature is that mail is grouped with its associated replies and attachments, such as a PC file, so that a user can ask to see all the comments and attachments associated with a specific message. In addition, when a user replies to a mail message, the screen is split so that the user can see the original message while creating the reply.

Although ADR/eMail does not support X.400, its architecture includes an eMail System Interface (ESI) that allows messages to be sent or received from other systems. The ESI, of course, must be customized for each system to which it communicates. ADR/eMail can also send IBM OS data sets, including reports that are already stored to disk in a print format and data that is generated for another application, such as a business form.

ADR/eMail's directory is built into the mail system, along with a sophisticated accounting system. The directory allows alphanumeric names and aliases so that a user can be reached by a nickname as well as by a given name. The alias function can also be used to assign the name of a function to a specific individual. For example, each department can have a representative designated by the system so that when a message is sent to that department, it appears in a specific individual's mailbox. Users also keep a profile in the system that allows the selection of an output printer, choice of prompts, the date format, and message format control characters. The accounting system allows for departmental bill-back.

ADR/eMail can network among sister products running on other IBM mainframes. In such networks, the directory is duplicated on each mail system in the network and can be kept in synchronization via automatic software routines that distribute changes to all the systems in the network. Pricing for ADR/eMail depends upon the operating system. A DOS version is priced at about $20,000, and OS and MVS versions are priced at about $40,000.

Data General's CEO

Data General's Comprehensive Electronic Office (CEO) is an integrated office system in which mail is one application. CEO is designed to run across Data General's range of minicomputers; thus, networking is an important element. Data General, in fact, has licensed X.400 from Sydney Development Corp. and has already introduced an X.400 gateway. Data General has also announced that it will incorporate X.400 as part of its basic version of CEO's mail capabilities.

CEO itself supports word processing, decision support, business graphics, and data base access as well as mail. Because the system is designed as a primary tool for creating documents and spreadsheets and accessing data bases, the mail system supports the transfer of all these document types. CEO distinguishes between three types of messages that can be sent. The first type is a short message that can be up to nine lines long. It is created using a limited text editor. The second is a document that can be of unlimited length and is created with the system's word processor. The third is any file on the system, which is transmitted using a specific command to send a file. Messages can be designated as certified, confidential, or urgent. A user can also send a message acting for another person who is away.

Data General has built a gateway into CEO to allow connection to MCI Mail and also has gateways to private mail systems, including

IBM's DISOSS. Data General has also integrated IBM PC files into CEO so that they can be transmitted via the system.

CEO's directory is designed so that it must be replicated on each system within the network. This enables every user to find out the name of every other user on the network. People whose names are in the directory have alphanumeric names and can also designate nicknames. Users can create distribution lists that are private or registered for others on the system to use. CEO comes with an accounting system, although it operates on a per node basis.

Pricing for CEO is about $20,000 for a system running on Data General's AOS operating system and $26,000 for the AOS/VS system. Additional modules include word processing and information management.

Digital Equipment's ALL-IN-1

Digital's ALL-IN-1 is an integrated office system that competes directly with Data General's CEO and Hewlett-Packard's DeskManager III. Applications include electronic mail, calendaring, a telephone directory, action item list, decision support, word processing, and data base access. ALL-IN-1 can operate across Digital's wide range of VAX computers and with Digital's Message Router so that large mail networks can be developed. Digital has announced that it is migrating its present mail systems and its Message Router to full X.400 compatibility. In this way, ALL-IN-1's mail system will serve as a user agent within an overall X.400 network. Digital presently has an X.400 software gateway available that can interact with its Message Router software. ALL-IN-1 also has gateways into the telex network and to MCI Mail.

The mail system itself can handle a variety of different files, including Digital's WPS word processor, ASCII messages, and other formatted VAX files. Using PC ALL-IN-1, IBM PC files can also be transferred via the system, although only to other PC ALL-IN-1 users. ALL-IN-1 mail supports all common mail functions, including reading, sending, forwarding, replying to, filing, and deleting messages.

Its directory allows users without mailbox addresses to be listed in the directory, with messages being sent to an output printer located in a specific department or the mailroom. In this way, everyone in the organization can receive messages via the mail system. Because networking is an important element of ALL-IN-1, the directory is designed to operate with duplicated directories on every system in the network—which is the way most mail systems handle networked systems—or as part of a backbone mail system in which directory names are distributed across the network. Pricing for ALL-IN-1 begins at the $15,000 range per system.

Digital recently announced a major upgrade, called MAILbus, to its electronic mail product line. MAILbus is a networked message transport capability based on Message Router that allows electronic mail systems from multiple vendors to be integrated into a single network. MAILbus features a distributed directory across the network, network administration from a central location and interconnections for a variety of systems, including IBM's PROFs and DISOSS, MCI Mail, Verimation's MEMO, any system that supports X.400 and Digital's own User Agents, including ALL-IN-1, VMS Mail and ULTRIX Mail Plus.

MAILbus represents an important new direction for vendors in the industry because it separates an electronic mail User Agent, such as ALL-IN-1, from the Message Transfer Agent as part of a native mail architecture, making the message transport a separate product in its own right.

Hewlett-Packard's HPDeskmanager III

Hewlett-Packard's mail system is the HPDeskmanager III, which is part of an integrated office system that competes with Digital Equipment and Data General offerings. HPDeskmanager III includes electronic mail, filing, and time management. The system is designed to operate in a networked environment. Hewlett-Packard, for example, operates its own internal network with more than 30,000 users in 250 locations. The system is integrated into the telex network via HPTelex II software. In addition, Hewlett-Packard has a Foreign Service Connection (FSC) capability that allows it to use the ARPA Internet file interface format to send messages to other systems. Hewlett-Packard also has an X.400 gateway.

HPDeskmanager III can handle the transmission of ASCII messages, along with formatted files from a variety of different applications software, including IBM PC software. Users can create personal distribution lists for storage in a special list area or in an electronic filing cabinet. HPDeskmanager supports a rich set of mail commands, including the ability of the sender to be separate from the message's author, which allows a secretary to edit a document and send it for its original author. A user can also designate someone to perform work on his or her behalf, such as editing a document or reading mail. Mail designated as private cannot be read by a designee. Finally, a user on vacation can have all mail forwarded to another user or have a reply generated to all messages that the user is unavailable to answer messages for a specific period.

As HPDeskmanager is designed to operate in large multinodal networks, it features a centralized directory that can be searched to find the name and nodal address of any user. HPDeskmanager also has a General Delivery Mail Box facility that allows a message for a user whose mailbox location is not known to be forwarded to a printer for printing and physical delivery. The General Delivery capability can also be used to send mail to people who do not have mailboxes.

HPDeskmanager III is priced at $12,000 for the first system, with other systems in the network priced at $8,400. Other modules, such as HPTelex II, HPWord, HPDraw, and other members of its integrated office series, have separate prices.

International Business Machines' PROFs

IBM has two separate mail systems: PROFs and DISOSS, which are the systems for IBM's Personal Services/370. PROFs operates under the VM/CMS operating system, and DISOSS operates under MVS, DOS, and OS. Although PROFs and DISOSS were once very different, they have been moving closer together in recent years in both appearance and features. When IBM's System Application Architecture (SAA) is implemented with a Common User Interface, the two systems may end up looking identical.

PROFs offers electronic mail, time management, calendaring, and electronic filing, with IBM's Displaywrite/370 as the integrated word processor. PROFs users can send three types of messages: a message, which is up to three lines long and is delivered to another user on the system in real-time; a note, which is created directly in a limited full-screen editor within PROFs, with the address entered at time of creation; and a document, which uses the system's word processor and can have predefined addressing information.

PROFs is designed to be operated in a full-screen 3270 terminal environment, with extensive use made of the terminal's function keys. It can be accessed in line-by-line mode by IBM 3101 terminals, although users must enter commands directly without using any of the system's menu capabilities. PROFs provides users with a basic complement of electronic mail capabilities, including *send, receive, forward, file,* and *delete.* Although PROFs was initially designed to work solely with DCF as the word processor, it has been enhanced so that it now supports Displaywrite/370 as the word processor of choice. Other word processors can also be substituted. As an example, WordPerfect Corp. plans to create a mainframe version of its popular WordPerfect word processor that can be substituted as PROFs' word processor.

PROFs does not handle the transfer of IBM PC files. This must be done via another module on the network.

PROFs can operate in a multinode network, although it does not yet provide a networked directory. In fact, PROFs does not use an internal directory. Instead, it operates as an application within the general directory provided by the VM/CMS operating system so that other applications can be keyed to the same directory. The system's operator, however, must write a routine to allow the directory to be searched. Although IBM does not yet supply any gateways to other services, numerous third-party companies have built gateways to communicate with PROFs. As an example, Western Union can exchange telex messages with a PROFs node without any software enhancements to the IBM system. Western Union has emulated a PROFs node as part of its Easylink service so that PROFs will transfer messages as if it were sending them to another node.

IBM has extensive plans to enhance the flexibility and networking capabilities of PROFs. As an example, it plans to network PROFs nodes and DISOSS nodes together via its SNADS software so that messages and computer files can be exchanged across both systems. It also plans a networkwide directory so that users can identify mail users operating on other nodes.

PROFs is priced at $750 per month per system on a lease from IBM or $21,000 for a one-time fee. The word processor module is additional.

Verimation's MEMO

Verimation is a joint subsidiary of Swedish companies Volvo and L.M. Ericsson. The mail system, MEMO, operates on IBM mainframes running under the MVS operating system. MEMO is written in Assembler to run directly under IBM's Virtual Telecommunications Access Monitor (VTAM), which makes it one of the most efficient systems on the market. It was developed initially as an internal system for Volvo and was so successful that other companies began asking for copies. Volvo set up a group to sell the software and eventually entered into a joint marketing arrangement with Ericsson. Although MEMO is a newcomer to North America, entering the market in 1987, it is one of the most popular systems in Europe with more than 350,000 users.

MEMO is a unique mail system because it has only one mailbox that houses all messages regardless of their status. The mailbox has six different statuses: *sent to, received from, received/read, selected by, saved memo,* and *follow up.* The user can alter the status mask so that the inbox only displays messages with that specific status.

MEMO also has a unique method for users to reply to messages. When the user specifies a reply, the original message is placed in the editor. The user can then add a reply at the top or the bottom of the message. This allows a single file to build up with multiple responses, which gives the user a good historical look at how a single message progresses into one with multiple replies. MEMO does not have a forward command. Forwards are done by loading text from one message into a new message and by sending it to a new recipient.

There is one aspect of MEMO's reply capability that is controversial. MEMO does not protect the sanctity of an original message. The user is placed in the editor with the original message during replies, making it possible to change the original's content. This is unique in the market amongst major systems. Every other system prevents messages from being altered. If a message must be edited, other systems make it possible to move the text into the editor. The resulting message can only be sent out, however, as a new message.

Messages are created in a simple editor provided within MEMO. The editor has a limit of 700 lines. It is also possible to use a more comprehensive word processor developed by Volvo. In both cases, wordwrap is available to users with entry assist on their controllers. MEMO also has a MEMO/PC package that emulates the system's interface on a PC. Messages are read and created offline. Only ASCII files, however, can be transferred to MEMO.

MEMO has a global mailbox concept that is the equivalent of a bulletin board system. The global mailbox can also be used to publish distribution lists or business forms. Users can create their own forms directly within MEMO. The forms have protected fields and constructs, such as calculations. They also can have specified routing pathways. Forms can be sent directly to users or copied from a global mailbox.

MEMO has extensive networking capabilities and allows MEMOs operating on different mainframes to be networked together. The system keeps copies of the full directory on all nodes and has routines that automatically distribute changes to any individual directory. MEMO also has gateways available to the telex network, GE Information Services' Quik-Comm, and Digital Equipment's Message Router. Plans are underway to add SNADS and X.400 gateways as well. MEMO also has an Application Program Interface (API) that allows custom gateways to be built between other message systems or application programs. This not only allows MEMO to be interfaced to other mail systems, but it also allows other applications to use MEMO as a means of routing reports and other data.

PCC Systems' cc:Mail

PCC Systems has a LAN-based electronic mail package called cc:Mail. It is included here to illustrate the difference between minicomputer, or mainframe, CBMS and LAN-based software. In general, minicomputer and mainframe-based electronic mail is designed as part of an integrated office system, with users expected to operate via a hardwired connection. Most of the systems, however, can also be accessed in line mode at slower speeds, although services are substantially reduced.

cc:Mail is designed to be used exclusively on a LAN and to integrate the creation of multimode PC files. Users are beeped when they receive messages and have the ability to interrupt the program that they are working on to look at the message's header, then return to the same point in the program. When users access cc:Mail remotely from a PC with a modem, their files are transferred via an error-free protocol so that they can be handled offline.

cc:Mail has its own built-in full-screen editor that is similar to a simple PC word processor; it also has a graphics editor similar to Apple's MacPaint program. The editors do not replace the user's personal word processor or graphics packages but serve as tools to integrate multiple PC files together as attachments in a single message. During the creation of a message, any number of PC files can be linked as attachments. cc:Mail also has a utility that runs on the PC in background so that a user can take a snapshot of any screen and make the snapshot an attachment as well. The snapshot is limited to one screen. This allows cc:Mail to be used for simple messages of a few lines or extremely complex, multifile messages.

cc:Mail is designed to be used between PCs directly or via a LAN as a central server. LAN servers can also work together in a network of cc:Mail systems. Users have the ability to create distribution lists and also to create their own file folders where messages are stored. In addition, each system has a directory of up to 250 users, although there are no provisions for operating the directory across multiple nodes. cc:Mail also has a central accounting package that identifies usage statistics and has diagnostic utilities to help maintain the message data base, which operates with a similar architecture to larger mail systems. cc:Mail also has a gateway to IBM's PROFs so that users can exchange messages between a PROFs system and cc:Mail system.

cc:Mail is priced at $795 for a 10-user version, including administrator software. Incremental users can be added for $395 per five users. An unlimited server license is $2,495.

Evolution of Private Systems

During the next few years, there will be major changes in the private systems market, primarily related to the issue of interconnection and PC integration. Mainframe- and minicomputer-based mail systems will substantially improve their ability to integrate PC files, with the better systems adopting the concept of attached PC files to basic messages. The leading systems will also adopt network-oriented features, such as networked directories and accounting subsystems. Gateways will also be an important issue. Although many of these packages will support X.400, they will also develop special gateways between leading packages as an interim step until X.400 is well established in the market. These packages are also likely to interconnect to facsimile machines, telex networks, and leading public services as well as to other in-house products.

There will also be a major change in LAN-oriented mail systems, which will move into a second development phase. In the first phase, LAN mail systems duplicated the basic features of larger CBMS, with the added twist of allowing PC files to be sent as attachments to a basic message. In their second phase, LAN systems will use the emerging base of 80386 microcomputers to enhance their operations considerably via increased processing speed. Most LAN mail developers will build gateways to popular mainframe or minicomputer-based systems and will also incorporate X.400 capability so that they can function within an X.400 network. These systems will also develop improved accounting software and inter-LAN directories so that system planners can derive operating statistics for networked mail operations and provide users with better directory capabilities.

In conclusion, the private CBMS software industry is now in what might be called a network development phase. Although the last five years has been a period in which basic capabilities and interconnections were developed, the next five years will see the PC integrated into mail systems, and interconnection capabilities mature into full networking capabilities, including networked directories and accounting systems. The purpose, of course, will be to serve network planners as well as individual mail users.

CBMS Applications, Costs, and Justification

Computer-based message systems play three roles inside organizations. CBMS serve as:

- A new means of interpersonal communication;
- A general medium for transferring computer files, business forms, and batch data files; and
- A means of interconnecting separate message and document transfer networks such as facsimile, telex, and teletex.

This powerful capability allows a CBMS to be used as a generic communications tool, which means that it has widespread applicability inside most businesses. In fact, it is appropriate for planners to search for applications within every white collar department within the organization. Planners should be aware, however, that CBMS are so generic in their capability that it is sometimes hard to come up with any single example that typifies overall use of the technology. Instead, the value of a CBMS is in its ability to handle a wide range of communications.

Applications for CBMS

Computer mailbox systems are used generically for a wide variety of formal and informal communications in much the same way that telephones or written memos are used as generic communication tools. Table 8-1 lists some of the more visible applications for a CBMS on a functional basis throughout five key departments in most organizations. The list is anything but exhaustive, but it at least provides a sample of the wide variety of uses.

The table identifies a number of situations where a computer mailbox system is particularly effective. For personal communications, a CBMS is particularly effective when a group of people is involved in coordinating activities or when the information is time-sensitive. The value for group communications lies in the fact that the same message can be effortlessly sent to a number of people, which improves their span of knowledge about group activities. The value of a CBMS for time-sensitive information comes from the CBMS' time and distance independence.

Table 8-1. Typical Applications of a CBMS

Department	Typical Applications
Sales	Sending price changes, new product announcements, availability information, sales status and other time-sensitive info to sales force; reception of inquiries, orders, status requests and performance reports from sales force; coordination of shipping and customer service activities from various departments; sending thank you letters, shipping confirmations and responses to inquiries from customers; receiving general inquiries from customers
Marketing	Coordination with field sales force, advertising, engineering and other departments; contact with consultants and other info providers; requests for information from sources inside and outside the company
Finance	Reception of time sheets, P.O. requests, requisition forms, orders, financial reports and other formal communications from various departments
Engineering	Communication with subcontractors, including change orders, performance reports, status inquiries; coordination of activities with manufacturing, including trouble reports, bug reporting, general inquiries.
Research & Development	General coordination of projects with R&D staff and other key departments; transmission of info requests and performance reports.

A CBMS is also valuable for formal communications, such as orders, purchase order requisitions, periodic performance reports, shipping inquiries and notices, financial information, and other business forms that often languish for days inside a physical delivery system. The reason is almost self-evident. A communication for which time is a factor is a candidate for transmission via a CBMS. PCs further enhance the value of a CBMS by serving as the front end for filling out the form or report. Many of the better CBMS, for example, have their own business forms capabilities, although the forms must be filled out sequentially, prompt by prompt. PCs allow the same forms to be filled out in a full-screen format, which makes it easier for the user.

Span of Communications

When CBMS were first employed, their greatest value was seen to be—and has been proven true—in long distance communications; e.g., for people in different facilities, especially those across many time zones. CBMS have also proven to be effective tools for communication between planning teams in contiguous offices in the same building because of the CBMS' ability to increase the group's span of knowledge about each member's activities. Usage also does not have to be restricted to employees in the same company. CBMS have been used quite effectively by numerous companies for communications with customers, subcontractors, outside suppliers, consultants, the press, and other non-employees. Intercompany applications range from interpersonal messaging to the transmission of reports, inquiries, shipping, dunning notices, new product announcements, general product information, and customer orders.

Elemental vs. Strategic Applications

The types of applications listed above are elemental because they are discrete examples of information that can be communicated independent of any other frame of reference. There is another type of application, however, in which the CBMS becomes part of a series of tools that are integrated to solve higher level strategic problems. To give one example, a sales department's main strategic goal for the year might be to improve the turnover rate of its inventory. To accomplish this, the company might create a data base of inventory items, along with a number that it considers high for each specific item. Those items that go above their accepted level will be selected in a daily or weekly report. The data base might then automatically search a customer list to find customers who regularly purchase those items and generate an electronic mail message to the sales people responsible for the accounts, with electronic copies going to their sales managers and national headquarters. The sales people can then call the customers, offering the overstocked items at a reduced rate. As a variation, the data base system might generate a special sales letter to each customer offering the overstocked items at a special sales rate. The letters would be sent in batch to the CBMS where they would be transferred to a public electronic mail service that generated next-day business letters, asking each customer to call an 800 number to place an order.

The above example shows how strategic applications are developed by taking a goal and integrating the appropriate technologies required to meet it. Most departments will be able to identify elemental applications for electronic mail themselves once they understand the basic value of a CBMS. These departments, however, may need help in putting together the series of tools that are usually required for a strategic application.

Another way to look at this is through the steps that are required for most strategic applications. In general, strategic applications will always require the acquisition, presentation, and communication of information. Electronic mail will usually be valuable for communication, but data bases, word processing, and other tools will be required for the acquisition and presentation. The first role of central planning is to make sure that the individual tools are integrated properly so that a complete application can be developed. The second role is to work directly with user departments to understand their strategic goals and to help the departments assemble the appropriate tools to meet those goals.

Data Base and CBMS Connection

The strongest applications will usually require integrating information from data bases with electronic communications. Most CBMS, however, were developed as separate communication tools; thus, they require customized integration via an application shell that runs either on the host computer or PC front end software. Central electronic mail planners should anticipate this need and work with other technology planning groups inside the organization, such as the Information Center, to be ready to handle the development of these applications as required. Unfortunately, this is not the typical way that most electronic mail planning teams operate. Instead of looking for strategic applications, with a ready plan to integrate data base access with a CBMS, they usually look for elemental applications that do not require such integration because their system is not set up to handle it. There is little doubt, however, that companies who forge a connection between their key data bases and CBMS will be able to develop integrated applications with far more value to users.

Typical Usage Patterns

One of the most commonly asked questions about CBMS usage is, "What is a typical usage pattern?" Because there are no official statistics in the industry about average usage, most organizations do not know how their electronic mail usage compares with usage on other systems. For this book, more than a dozen companies were interviewed about their usage patterns, including several vendors who shared information on what they believed to be typical patterns based upon aggregate usage across their customer bases. Because most of these companies considered the information proprietary, specific names are not included. Unfortunately, the results varied so widely that it is difficult to come up with a definitive answer to average usage.

There are, however, several generalizations that can be made. First, public services tend to have considerably lower average session times than in-house systems, even though the number of sessions per month per user is consistent. Second, applications, such as sending specialized business forms, have more widely different usage patterns than general usage by managers and professionals who use the mail system to replace writing paper memos or using the telephone. Third, there are wildly diverging distribution patterns of usage across user bases. On some public services, for example, there are no problems with users checking their mailboxes regularly, whereas there are on other public services. The same is true of in-house systems. In general, the tighter a company controls issuing passwords and monitoring usage, the more likely it will be that most users sign on regularly.

Although it is impossible to create an industry average because usage patterns are so divergent, it is possible to identify a typical usage pattern based on an aggregation of patterns from the companies that were interviewed. The pattern, which is shown in Figure 8-1, is more of a midpoint than a formal industry average. The pattern distributes usage across a base of 500 total users. The **X**-axis shows the distribution of users into four groupings based on the number of times the user signed on, and the **Y**-axis shows the total number of hours per month that each group used the mail system. The usage pattern, incidentally, is only for sending electronic mail messages and does not include either data base or bulletin board access.

For Figure 8-1, the major variable is the number of sessions held per month, and the constant is the average session time, which is the time that the user spends online. An average session time of 7 minutes is used, which is a somewhat arbitrary number. Average session times amongst the systems studied ranged from a low of of 4 minutes to a high of 12 minutes. Interestingly, both the low and high average session times were on private systems. In general, however, most of the people interviewed believed that session times on private systems tend to be longer than on public services, especially on those that charge by the hour.

Figure 8-1. CBMS Usage Across a Base of 500 Users

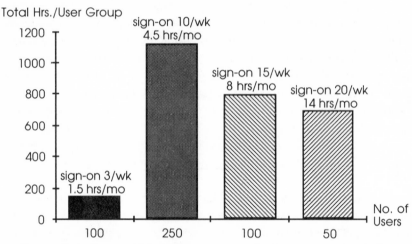

As Figure 8-1 shows, 100 users sign on only 3 times per week for total usage of about 1.5 hours per month per user. These are the infrequent users who are common on many systems, especially those operated in-house without close monitoring from administrators. There are 250 users— the overwhelming majority— who sign on twice a day on average, with average usage of about 4.5 hours per month. There are also 100 users who sign on about 3 times per day and have average usage of 8 hours per month. Finally, there are 50 users who sign on an average of 4 times per day for average usage of 14 hours per month. These users often are involved in specific applications that result in heavier usage, such as using business forms.

Impact of PCs on Usage Patterns

Although the usage pattern in Figure 8-1 is a classic one that is likely close to many CBMS operations, the PC will almost certainly change this pattern significantly. As an example, one large microcomputer company operates a network on a public CBMS service for about 2,500 internal users and an equal number of dealers, consultants, and software developers. Every user on the system has sophisticated PC front end software that allows mail-related interactions to be performed offline. Accessing data bases and bulletin boards, however, is performed while online. During the month, the "average" user on this system signed on 37 times (1.7 times per day), with an average session time of about 7 minutes. The "average" user read 84 messages and sent 21, with an average of 4 recipients per message. Users also made an average of 30 data base or bulletin board accesses per month.

In the above example, advanced PC software has had a levelling impact on CBMS usage by making it easier for low volume users to interact with the system and by defraying the time that heavy users must interact with the system. Although the PC software obviously lowers the cost of reading and creating messages, it also seems to increase overall usage by making it easier to use the mail system. In general, however, there is mounting evidence that PCs tend to reduce overall session times. One vendor, for example, which introduced an advanced PC software package several months ago, has noticed session times declining slowly, but steadily.

Data Base and Bulletin Board Integration

The trend toward integrating data base access and bulletin boards with CBMS is also having a significant impact on usage. On the microcomputer network described above, for example, roughly 30 percent of usage is attributed to data base access. One major CBMS public service vendor with bulletin boards that has tracked usage closely during the last several years has experienced a similar trend in usage, as has Hewlett-Packard, which recently ran a trial of an electronic mail and data base access system for its sales force. In the trial, which was used by 100 sales representatives, 71 percent of the accesses were mail related, 22 percent were related to checking order status, and 7 percent were related to checking pricing.

Identifying Costs of CBMS

Identifying average usage is only one part of the problem facing electronic mail planners, who must also monitor the costs and justify usage of their mail systems. Monitoring costs seems easy enough within one organization. The problem is that no industry average cost statistics exist to provide planners with a frame of reference for comparison with others in the industry. Justifying a CBMS is also a very difficult task because of the many variables that must be controlled to obtain hard dollar justification.

To put this into perspective, however, justifying the telephone is just as difficult. In fact, I have never seen a study that identifies the hard dollar value of the telephone to a company, except in specific applications such as using the phone to improve credit collections. Nevertheless, no organization would pull out its phone system because it could not be justified in hard dollars. Furthermore, telephones have spread ubiquitously throughout companies without a formal cost justification. How did this happen?

Comparing CBMS to the Telephone

Although we take the telephone for granted today, in the early 1950s few companies made telephones available to all white collar employees. According to statistics from the Bureau of the Census, there were about 60 million people in the U.S. labor force in 1955 and 109 million in 1980. According to statistics from the Federal Communications Commission, the labor force in 1955 had an estimated 28 million telephones whereas the labor force in 1980 had an estimated 85 million. In short, the percentage of telephones to employees rose from 46 percent in 1955 to 78 percent in 1980.

Given that the benefit of the telephone has never been given a quantified, hard dollar value, why did its usage grow? The reason is simple. Managers trusted their common sense and decided that the likelihood that productivity would improve by putting telephones on everyone's desk was worth the risk of the capital investment per employee. The same is true of CBMS today. As with the telephone, managers are recognizing that a CBMS is valuable and are trying to contain its costs rather than justify its usage. This, of course, means that planners need a solid grasp of the costs for a CBMS, along with a plan to monitor performance and control those costs.

Costs of a CBMS

Table 8-2 identifies the major cost elements of a typical CBMS operated on an in-house basis. The required elements and their cost ranges were assembled based on discussions with a number of vendors and users. The elements include host CBMS software; hardware costs for the host computer and its front end telecommunications network to support a simultaneous user (called port cost); modem and PC software costs or terminal costs for each user; communications usage costs to access the CBMS; and staff costs for planning, implementing, and operating the system. Public CBMS services, of course, have a different cost structure. Instead of paying for host-related hardware and software, the user pays usage rates in the range of $15 to $20 per hour per user.

Table 8-2. Costs of Electronic Mailbox System

Item	Cost	Description
Software	$5,000-$40,000	Range for a CPU license
Port Cost	$3000-$6,000	Per port cost, including modem, channel and host processing
Modems & PC Software	$225-$500	Cost for 1,200 bps-2,400 bps modem & software
Communications	$0-$6/hour	Line usage cost that varies with access method
Personnel		
Operator	$26,000/year	Handles operations & software maintenance
Manager	$40,000/year	Responsible for planning and implementing system
Support Staff	$25,000/year	Responsible for training & liason with end users
Additional Staff	$25,000/year	As required to implement and operate system

The costs, incidentally, do not include staff costs for non-dedicated administrative support or the cost for training and advertising materials. Non-dedicated administrative support usually includes secretaries or administrative assistants who assume responsibility for certain training and operational details; training materials, such as manuals, typically cost in the $10 to $30 range per copy.

Per User Costs for a CBMS

The cost items in Table 8-2 can be translated into a monthly cost range for a CBMS on a per user basis by determining the capital investment required for host hardware, modems, PC software, host software, plus the operating costs for staff and communications, then dividing by the total number of users, as illustrated in Figure 8-2. The amortization rate for the high cost range is three years, and the amortization rate for the low cost range is five years.

As ports can be shared by multiple users as long as they are not hardwired to the host, each port's cost is shared by an average of 10 users in Figure 8-2, which is the average of the estimates given by the people interviewed to compile numbers for this section. The estimates ranged from a low of 6 users per port to a high of 50 users for public services that have a large number of users who sign on infrequently.

Figure 8-2. Monthly Per User Cost Range for In-House CBMS

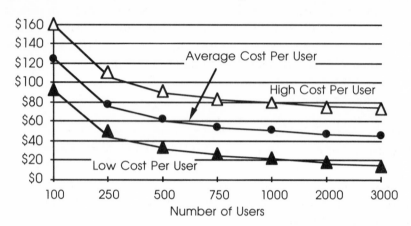

In the low cost figure, it is assumed that the system operates exclusively in a single building with no ongoing communication line costs; in the high cost scenario, it is assumed that all users operate on a packet or leased line network with a communication cost of $6 per hour. Average usage is assumed to be 4 hours per user per month across the total base of users. This average usage rate was chosen based upon a survey of several operational mail systems and can vary substantially, depending upon the system. The monthly cost range per user for a typical CBMS installed in-house is estimated in Figure 8-2.

As Figure 8-2 shows, the cost to set up and operate a CBMS in-house ranges from a low of about $19 per user per month for a system with 3,000 users to a high of about $160 per user per month for a system with 100 users. In practice, monthly per user costs for most companies will fall somewhere in the middle. As soon as the number of users reaches the 250 range, for example, the curve starts to flatten so that a typical in-house CBMS will cost in the range of $40 to $60 per user per month, provided that the company uses a capital investment payback period of three to five years.

Readers should keep in mind, however, that average usage statistics are still relatively sparse in the industry. Regardless, the above analysis has proven accurate with several users, such as Bankers Trust, which has a cost of $65 per user per month. Nevertheless, readers should take the above cost analysis as a starting point to develop industry averages, not as a definitive analysis.

Planners should also keep in mind that this cost includes only direct users with either terminals or PCs. A good CBMS, however, should include IDs for everyone in the organization whether or not he of she is a direct user. When messages are sent to non-direct users, they should be printed out in the company's mailroom and delivered as paper memos. This adds a cost to administering the system's directory but does not increase the actual hardware or software cost of the CBMS, provided that the software supports such a feature. In effect, it solves a major problem in spreading the CBMS throughout the organization without adding significantly to the costs of the system.

Using Public Services

Figure 8-2 assumes that the company operates its CBMS in-house. Many firms, however, operate using public services such as Easylink, MCI Mail, Telemail or Envoy 100—particularly when the CBMS is in the trial stage, has only a small number of total users, has a policy of avoiding its own computer operations, or has its users widely dispersed geographically.

Although there is no question that it is less costly to operate an in-house CBMS when the number of users reaches the 250 range, many companies prefer the reliability of operating on a public electronic mail service, which often has redundant, non-stop processors and mirrored disks that guarantee high message reliability and an uptime rate above 99.9 percent. Most in-house CBMS do not have the same reliability factors. Many other companies do not want the operational hassles of running an in-house mail system. Thus, there are many organizations that have several thousand users operating on a public service. Although it would be more cost-effective for these firms to operate their own mail system, they are quite content to operate on public services.

In general, a typical usage pattern for general messaging on a public CBMS results in a cost of from $60 to $80 per month per user. This, of course, can vary widely depending upon the application. The company, however, must still pay the cost of a modem and PC software for each user, along with ongoing staff costs to plan and administer the system. Although a system operator is not required, the company still must have a manager and at least one person to help with system administration and planning. This places public services costs in the $90 to $120 per month range per user for a system with from 100 to 500 users.

If a company decides to use a public service, one problem that planners will encounter is comparing costs. The public services do not have uniform pricing structures. As an example, BT Dialcom and Telemail have rate structures based primarily on usage time, whereas MCI Mail and Geisco have structures based on transactions. The only way to compare costs is to estimate typical usage patterns that include the cost elements used by the various service suppliers and then map the tariffs from the different suppliers to these patterns.[1]

Per Message Costs

One of the most frequent questions asked by planners is what is the cost of sending a message, which is often compared with the cost of sending a letter by traditional means. Although this is not a good way of justifying the costs of a CBMS because of the other shadow functions that are involved, Figure 8-3 compares the transmission cost of a 500-character message via an internal CBMS, telex, USPS first class letter, and internal mail system.

Figure 8-3. Comparative Message Transmission Costs

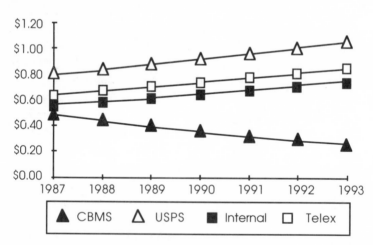

The figure also projects the average increase or decrease in costs over several years. CBMS costs, for example, which are based on electronics items such as computers and modems, are conservatively declining at a rate of about 10 percent per year, whereas the other systems, which are based on either manual delivery (internal and postal service mail) or an aging technology (telex), are increasing at a conservative rate of about 5 percent per year. Western Union, for example, recently increased its telex rate from 35¢ to 46¢ per minute. The

CBMS costs are based on a midrange system with 500 users as defined in Figure 8-2.

Figure 8-3 shows that the cost of an average CBMS message is now about 48¢ compared to 80¢ for a USPS first class stamp, 56¢ for sending a message by an internal mail system, and 65¢ to send the message by telex. As can be seen, a CBMS already is less expensive than the other delivery media because of the shadow functions that are eliminated. While a USPS stamp is 22¢, for example, the envelope is 10¢ and the secretary's time (three minutes at $20,000 per year) is 48¢, which totals about 80¢ to send a letter. Readers should be aware, however, that these numbers are quite arbitrary and are also situational. While the concept of average in electronic mail can be used to show a trend, a company must study its own environment to determine real costs.

The lower cost of sending a memo via a CBMX versus an internal paper mail system, furthermore, cannot be used as part of a cost displacement justification for a CBMS because the costs do not really displace each other. The CBMS, secretary, and internal mail paper system have fixed costs that will not vary based on cross-elastic usage. Instead, the company will have the same costs for the secretary and internal mail system regardless of CBMS usage. The value of the secretary's time and the value of delivering memos faster, however, are a proper part of a CBMS cost justification.

Justifying the Costs for a CBMS

Identifying and measuring the costs for a CBMS, of course, are only one half the battle. The real difficulty is in settling the question of whether those costs are justified by improving the productivity of users. At this point, a hard reality enters the picture: It is difficult, if not impossible, to cost justify a CBMS using hard dollar cost displacement or value-added justification methods. The variables are too complex. How do managers determine to the penny whether it is worth from $60 to $100 per month per user to provide a computer mailbox service to users in the company?

Management, at this point, has a choice. It can either accept that it is almost impossible to perform any formal justification, as it did with the telephone, and focus its efforts on cost containment, or it can spend some effort trying to quantify as best as possible that its investment in a CBMS will yield improved productivity. Most companies with CBMS in operation have created estimates of the benefits by sending out user questionnaires and by performing a soft dollar justification, but few, if any, have gone much beyond this method of justification. The reason, incidentally, is that most companies become convinced of the benefits via a soft dollar justification largely based on the opinions of their users, and then prefer to focus on implementation rather than proving the benefits further.

For those firms who believe it necessary to quantify the value of electronic mail as best as possible, it is possible to identify certain statistics that may help to confirm the value of a CBMS. As an example, it should be possible to study the telephone records of CBMS and non-CBMS users to determine average usage patterns. Telephone usage should decrease for CBMS usage. A CBMS also has measurable time savings. A secretary assigned to five managers, for example, can be freed by 10 to 15 hours per month by eliminating the need to copy and help distribute memos. Managers are also saved something like 4 hours per month in administrative overhead by using a CBMS. These time savings can be confirmed via careful study. It also may be possible to determine the value of sending certain types of business forms on the system. When the time savings alone are added up, for example, a CBMS may displace up to several hundred dollars per month in management time value per user that can be spent in primary, rather than administrative, activities. It can also save a secretary $100 in time value per month by reducing administrative overhead for copying memos and answering return telephone tag calls.

Although these time savings are real, they do not represent an improvement in productivity in a classic sense. Factory output, for example, does not increase by $100 per employee, which is a real measure of productivity. Instead, a CBMS provides professional and managerial employees with the opportunity to spend perhaps 4 hours more per month on primary activities, and it frees secretaries to spend 10 hours per month on tasks that are not related to gross administrative work such as copying and answering telephones. Top management must decide whether it is worth paying a fixed cost of $50 per month per direct user for the opportunity to spend more time on primary activities.

The elemental time savings that come from a CBMS are difficult to translate into a cost justification because of the difficulty of evaluating whether each manager will actually invest the savings properly. When the elemental time savings are translated to a systems time savings, however, its value becomes clearer. Consider the case study of Beneficial Finance's use of electronic mail (see Chapter 1). In this example, key management gained access to critical information related to a multimillion dollar decision because of the mail system. It was not available any other way. To give another example, let's say that a key product reaches the market in 11 months instead of 12 because of the cumulated impact of using a CBMS. This certainly seems worth $50 per month per employee in a competitive market environment. There is no certainty, however, that the improved time savings actually result in increased revenues.

Cost Justification as a Risk Assessment

In the final analysis, management must decide whether the opportunity to improve productivity— and the potential benefits that might ensue— is worth incurring a cost in the range of $40 to $60 per month per direct user. This turns the cost justification of a CBMS into a classic risk assessment in which management must decide to risk its capital in expectation of a return. Normally, such assessments are made as part of a well defined marketing cycle in which the new product or service is tested via market research both as a concept and a prototype. Competitive factors also enter the picture; factors such as other companies in the market and the ability of the firm to manufacture the product at a competitive price. In the end, new products are introduced only after rigorous scrutiny. The irony, however, is that most new products still do not meet their expected goals despite the gauntlet that they run before their companies introduce them.

At this writing, no such well defined process exists for evaluating the risks of introducing a new technology into an organization. There is, however, a competitive imperative to keep pace with technological innovations if for no other reason than to protect against the downside of not employing a technology that competitors use to improve their productivity. As much as management may wish, it cannot ignore this competitive imperative to keep pace with the Joneses.

Competitive protection is a valid part of any decision to implement electronic mail because the risk factor is particularly low. Unlike investing in specialized equipment that may turn out to be a complete writeoff, for example, investing in the hardware required for electronic mail is a low risk. The host computer, for example, can be used for other applications if the system proves itself to be underutilized. Communication costs will also be low if the system does not meet expectations and is not used. In all, if a CBMS fails, it is likely to cost the company about $10 per user per month. If it succeeds, it could easily be worth $100 per user per month, giving the system a reward:risk ratio of 10:1. These are good odds in favor of implementing a CBMS.

Monitoring CBMS Performance

Although it may be pointless to look for a quantified cost justification of a CBMS, its managers should certainly adopt measures to monitor performance and control costs. The best method is through an accounting system that monitors usage. Unfortunately, this is easier said than done as most in-house CBMS software on the market does little more than provide planners with a picture of how long each user spends on the system. If a company invests in a CBMS across a large base of users, however, it should consider developing its own accounting system that matches its telephone usage control system. Such an accounting system would identify statistics such as the number of messages transmitted by type and length of message, the number of sign-ons on a daily basis, usage of the system's editor, usage of business forms, the number of copies of each message on average, usage of bulletin boards and data bases that are available for access, and the usage of offnet services such as a connection between the in-house service and a public messaging system.

In the hands of experienced personnel, these usage statistics can provide valuable insight into whether users are really deriving benefit from the system. If, as an example, there is a usage ratio of four copies of every message originated, which is typical for most CBMS, this means that the system is probably being used by planning teams to keep each other informed of activities. It is almost a certainty that the CBMS is valuable when used in this fashion. If there is a growing number of large files in the range of 5,000 characters and up that are being sent by the system, it likely means that the CBMS is being used instead of the internal mails or courier services, which is likely improving turnaround time of documents while also offsetting administrative staff time. To see if the time is being employed profitably, planners can contact the managers of these departments to see if administrative staff has been handed special assignments that have more value to the company than copying memos and answering telephones. In short, although a good accounting system does not prove that a system is justified, in creative hands, it can provide valuable clues to help the company assure proper usage.

Summary

Cost justifying a CBMS is a difficult task. After a careful analysis, however, it is almost a certainty that a CBMS will save its users a few hours per month in administrative overhead, while streamlining the flow of messages throughout an organization. In terms of a reward:risk ratio, a CBMS has a reasonable chance to improve productivity by roughly $100 per user per month, and its cost if it fails is roughly $10 per month per employee. Justifying a CBMS, however, is more than developing a theoretical reward:risk ratio. It requires a moderate course in which the company:

- Makes certain that it understands the benefits through a careful study of existing users, which includes hard usage statistics, well documented case studies, and a solid opinion survey of users;
- Defines its investment costs carefully and chooses an appropriate payback timeframe; and
- Develops a monitoring system to track usage and costs as the system expands.

Computer Conferencing

It was one of the most tense times of this decade. Russia had just shot down KAL 007, a Korean Airline 747 Jumbo jet that wandered over Soviet airspace on a flight from the United States to Korea.

Governments around the world were up in arms over the Soviet's action. Newspapers and televisions ran story after story about the incident. In a matter of days, KAL 007 became a household word.

During the same time, a new communications service was getting started on The Source, a public information and communications service that caters to home users. The service, called Participate, was a public computer conferencing service that allowed people to attend public meetings and exchange ideas worldwide.

Although it may have been preying upon misery, KAL 007's tragedy was the cause of a magic moment for about 100 telecommunications users in North America. From almost out of nowhere, experts in airlines operations and the military appeared on Participate to start an electronic discussion that lasted throughout the ensuing two weeks when KAL 007 was on everyone's mind. Everyone had a theory to expound about why and how it had happened. Could it have been an accident? Do commercial airlines carry out spy missions, as the Russians claimed? What goes on in the cockpit of a 747 when navigation courses are charted? How could the captain have made an error that led the plane into Soviet airspace? What should be done about it? Tempers flared. People with differing views clashed in print, but the end result was a remarkable exchange of information, ideas, and feelings.

As one of the participants in the KAL 007 conference, I became curious about the people who were obvious pioneers in a new medium. The service, Participate, has a capability that allows ballots and voting, so I did a quick demographic survey.[1] The results were not what one might expect. Instead of youthful hackers, 90 percent of the participants had completed a college degree, of which 60 percent had advanced degrees. Their average age was in the mid-30s, with almost 90 percent men. Their incomes averaged above $50,000 per year, with 25 percent making more than $75,000. Although

66 percent knew a computer language, only 40 percent were employed in the computer industry. Finally, 62 percent had never met another participant face to face, and 85 percent knew three people or less. Were it not for computer conferencing, the chances of their meeting to exchange information and ideas was virtually nil.

Development of Computer Conferencing

Computer conferencing has been around since the late 1960s when the Systems Evaluations Division of the Office of Emergency Preparedness in the Executive Office of the U.S. President contracted to develop a computer system to gather information on the wage-price freeze crisis that was then troubling the United States.[2] The result was a system called EMISARI, which was developed by Murray Turoff, who went on to make computer conferencing systems his career.

Turoff went from EMISARI to another conferencing system called DELPHI and ultimately developed the EIES system while working at the New Jersey Institute of Technology. EIES is probably the best known conferencing system in the world because of the well known book, *The Network Nation*, which Turoff co-authored with Starr Roxanne Hiltz, although EIES itself is a tiny service with about 1,000 users. During the same period as EIES was being developed, researchers at The Institute for the Future in Menlo Park, Calif., were working on two conferencing systems named Planet and Forum. Their research led to the development of the Notepad system, which is also offered publically today by Infomedia Corp. of Menlo Park, Calif.

The Enigma of Computer Conferencing

Although the power of computer conferencing to bring people together has been shown by the KAL 007 experience and many others, computer conferencing is an enigma. Historically, computer conferencing systems and CBMS are sister technologies, with CBMS improving productivity in individual communications (one person to another or to many people) and computer conferencing improving group communications (many people sharing the same information). From a theoretical viewpoint, furthermore, conferencing has the greater potential benefits because the needs for group interaction are greater in most environments than for individual communications.

Nevertheless, although the two types of computer-aided communications started the same way— with successful government and academic research projects in the late 1960s and early 1970s that spun off into commercial systems in the mid to late 1970s— CBMS have become firmly planted in the commercial environment while computer conferencing systems have the barest of toeholds. Statistically, for example, the EMA estimates about 1 million business users on public CBMS services in North America and 3.65 million users on in-house, private systems.

Although no one even keeps track of users on computer conferencing systems, the numbers are probably very low. My own survey of EIES, Infomedia and the several public services that run Participate for business users, for example, indicates that there are less than 20,000 users of these systems. Although there are dozens of well known companies with major in-house CBMS, there are only a handful of Fortune 500 companies— the best known being Procter & Gamble (P&G) and Hewlett-Packard— who can be considered major users of computer conferencing. P&G has more than 20,000 people on their own conferencing/mail system, and Hewlett-Packard has an estimated 5,000 users on an in-house version of CONFER, which is a conferencing system licensed from the University of Michigan. The most successful commercial computer conferencing system is VAX- Notes, which was introduced commercially in 1986 by Digital Equipment. According to several competitors, Digital sold several hundred copies in the first year that it was on the market. In contrast, however, Digital has more than 5,000 copies of its ALL-IN-1 mail system in operation.

In short, although both CBMS and computer conferencing have similar backgrounds, they have had very different development pathways. Although it is easy to write off the differences in usage as inherent to the technologies, the potential of computer conferencing to improve productivity in group activities is too powerful to ignore. People inside business organizations spend far more time in meetings and other group-related communication activities than they do writing memos or making telephone calls. It is an enigma why computer conferencing has not played a larger role in business organizations.

Success in Consumer Market

Conferencing, however, has developed a strong following on home-oriented consumer services such as The Source, CompuServe, and General Electric's Genie, which have a combined total of 500,000 users on their public conferencing services. Conferencing is also popular in academic and computer research environments, which have an estimated 100,000 users, and is growing in popularity with trade and non-profit associations and with religious groups, such as the Presbyterian Church, which has a nationwide conferencing system.

The greatest conferencing phenomenon, however, is the PC-based, public bulletin board systems, which are mushrooming at a phenomenal rate in North American cities. Bulletin board systems are a form of computer conferencing, despite the different name. In the past three years, more than 30,000 of these free (or very low cost) local systems have literally sprouted up. Although most are computer-club related, a growing number are being used for other applications, such as local politics and education. In Colorado Springs, Colo., for example, a well known conferencing pioneer, David Hughes, operates a multiuser bulletin board system to teach academic classes and has used it to fight local zoning and environmental issues.

Computer Conferencing Model

Computer conferencing offers an alternative model to CBMS, which use an inbox-desktop-outbox metaphor for handling messages. Computer conferencing uses the metaphor of a conference or meeting. Participants join the conference and follow the different topics inside. Topics consist of written responses from the participants, with each response entered in serial fashion. Conferencing gets its power from the ability of these meetings to transcend time and distance, with a written record of the conference being created as a by-product. People sign on at their own convenience (just as on a CBMS) and "attend" the conferences by reading the new discussion topics or new responses to existing topics, reviewing earlier discussions or responses, and then adding their own. Figure 9-1 shows the structure of a typical computer conferencing system.

As can be seen, a conferencing system is basically a hierarchical data base. The top level consists of conferences (meetings), the next level consists of topics (discussions), and the bottom level consists of responses (comments). This simple structure, however, can be quite deceiving in the more powerful conferencing systems that have controls placed on how people interact within each conference. It is possible on the better systems to control the hierarchical levels within a conference, along with the permissions to read and write. This allows conferencing systems to be used:

- As suggestion boxes;
- As bulletin boards;
- As open forums with unlimited topics; and
- As private meeting systems with a controlled agenda.

A suggestion box can be created by allowing everyone in the conference to write but allowing only the leaders to read what is written. A bulletin board can be created by allowing anyone to read the information, but only the leaders to create it (the opposite of a suggestion box). Open forums can be created by giving everyone read-write permission to create discussion topics and add comments. Private conferences can be created by allowing a sub-set of total users on the system to participate. The conference leaders can manage the meeting with further controls, such as by allowing only certain people to create discussion topics, but allowing anyone to make comments.

Figure 9-1. Model of Typical Computer Conferencing System

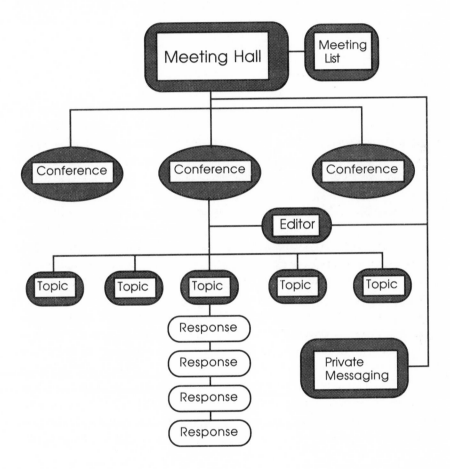

This type of control makes it possible to build a complete online environ-ment within one conferencing system, especially as the more powerful con-ferencing systems have additional features such as voting and CBMS-type electronic mail for private communication. This is an important point. Al-though most CBMS only have a single operational metaphor and means of threading the information (inbox-desktop-outbox and delivery), the more powerful conferencing systems allow multiple metaphors and threading pathways, which allow different types of interaction with the system, such as suggestion boxes, bulletin boards, private meetings, open forums, voting, and mail, each of which meets a specific information need. As an example, it is quite possible for a user to sign on to a conferencing system and in the same session:

- Read private messages;
- Attend an open brainstorming meeting;
- Enter a request for information in an open information-gathering meeting;
- Enter a suggestion into the suggestion box;
- Read public notices on the bulletin boards;
- Answer a questionnaire;
- Attend a few focused, private meetings; and
- Vote on some potential decisions in yet another meeting.

Attending an electronic computer conference is like reading a series of interrelated electronic mail messages. Each conference typically has a series of topics, with each topic housing the discussion point and the many responses from people attending the conference. Conferencing systems commands also have an overlap with CBMS commands. Most systems, for example, allow a person to read the responses, scan the different meetings for the topics that are available, create new discussion topics and reply to responses in a discussion topic.

This is what gives conferencing its group-related flavor. In a CBMS, each message is treated separately. If a message is sent to four people, for example, and they all make replies, the sender will see four separate messages in the inbox. Furthermore, if there are other messages that are sent in between the replies, the inbox will place the replies in the inbox based on when they were sent in relationship to other messages. In contrast, in a conferencing system, each comment is related to a specific topic.

Although conferencing systems manage the relationship of the responses and topics to a higher degree than does a CBMS, they too are far from perfect. Conferencing systems organize their topics and responses hierarchically, with time being the major variable. Topics and responses are numbered and positioned inside their conferences based on when they are entered. When the conferences are relatively small, the written record alone can be invaluable when new people join the group or when someone wants to refer back to a specific event or topic. As conferences grow in size, however, they can become overloaded with information, making it difficult for people to separate the valuable from the invaluable.

One of the great images in computer conferencing, for example, is the manager who hands a complete record of the conference to a business associate or new team member. By reading the record, the person can quickly become knowledgeable as to what is going on inside the business operation. Unfortunately, if the conference grows into hundreds of pages, few people have the time or inclination to read such a record. Although the better conferencing systems have some tools to help organize the information, such as the ability to create agendas, which are groupings of topics, conferencing systems are generally far better at collecting a large number of ideas than they are at sorting and categorizing the information.

Differences Between Conferencing and CBMS

There are both technical and social differences between CBMS and computer conferencing. As always, the technical differences are normally the ones that people focus on, whereas the social differences are ignored. Both differences, however, must be considered to explain why computer conferencing systems and CBMS have so far had very different development pathways in commercial, academic, and consumer environments.

Technical Differences

When the computer conferencing and CBMS models were first developed, there was a clear difference between the two systems. CBMS used the inbox-outbox model and were designed for one-to-one or one-to-many communications. Computer conferencing used the meeting model, which was designed for group interaction. In practice, however, today's better systems have merged bits and pieces of each so that the lines are very blurred.

Most CBMS, for example, have bulletin boards, which give them the ability to function as limited conferencing systems. In turn, most conferencing systems have the ability to deliver electronic mail for private communications. So the real technical differences between the better computer conferencing systems and CBMS today are where the emphasis is placed on their features and functions. At this writing, there is no system on the market that has integrated the two with a high degree of sophistication. Conferencing systems, for example, typically lack the forms, group messaging, and offnet delivery features of the more powerful CBMS. In turn, CBMS typically have bulletin board systems of limited power and lack the more sophisticated conferencing features, such as multiple metaphors and voting.

Social Differences

The social differences are similar to the differences associated with individual versus group communications. CBMS systems are very easy to use socially, especially as messages sent on a CBMS tend to be more informal than written memos. Organizational requirements for users are also minimal. Maintaining mailboxes, for example, typically takes only a few minutes per week. In fact, the social etiquette of CBMS usage tends to be far more forgiving than that of creating paper memos. Although few users will allow a printed memo to escape their offices with typos, spelling mistakes, or other errors, most CBMS have developed an ethic that forgives small errors because of the problems associated with typing. To put it another way, function very much follows form in CBMS— with form being a cross between the formality of a memo and the informality of a telephone call.

Computer conferencing is more resource-intensive than a CBMS, with users requiring considerably more skill to use the medium to its full potential. This is because meetings are far more complex events than memos or telephone calls, which are the major cross-elastic uses for CBMS. The differences are in the group dynamics associated with meetings, the amount of management skill required to hold successful meetings, and the additional technical skill required to control sophisticated conferencing systems.

Anyone who wants to control an online computer conference, for example, has to keep right on top of the meeting and guide it to reach its desired results; i.e., some set of conclusions about a problem or set of problems, along with a plan to solve the problem. Not only does this require general meeting leadership skills, but it also requires learning additional commands and skills to perform these tasks on a conferencing system. Because of these requirements, many conferences that start out with the goal of solving problems online end up as little more than brainstorming sessions, with key attendees becoming bored and dropping off as the value of the conference declines.

Nature of Conferencing Medium

Many people believe that part of conferencing's problem is related to the medium itself. Media differ in their characteristics so that some media are more suited to performing certain types of tasks than other media. It has long been known, for example, that television is a far more powerful medium for confirming existing opinions than for changing opinions or teaching new ideas.[3] To quote Gerhard Wiebe, a noted professor of communications:

> It is often said that media brings people into contact with each other. We must be more literal. The media transport only symbols. They do not bring people together. On the contrary, the media stand between people. The media may invite subsequent interaction, but they do not and cannot provide it.[4]

Many people, for example, believe that computer conferencing is not as good as a face-to-face meeting for reaching decisions. These people use this as the reason why conferencing has been successful in academic circles and consumer-oriented systems, where conferencing is used for information collection and interaction, but not in businesses, which are focused more on reaching decisions and taking action. Research into computer conferencing, however, shows a very different story. To cite one example, Starr Roxanne Hiltz wrote this about the ability of people to reach decisions on computer conferencing systems. Her comments are based on controlled experiments in which people participated in both computer conferences and face-to-face meetings:

> There is less tendency for a dominant person or leader to emerge in CC (computer conferencing), for "unstructured" conferences, in which no mechanism is provided to support emergence of a designated leader. We also found that there were, in fact, no statistically significant differences in the quality of decision reached. Both face-to-face and CC groups improved their decision about 25% as a result of their discussions.[5]

Basically, the existing research shows that conferencing is a poor medium in which to develop leaders within the conference. When used in an environment where there are clear leaders who assert their position, however, computer conferencing is almost as effective as face-to-face meetings for reaching decisions. The reason that computer conferencing has not been accepted inside business organizations is undoubtedly related more to a lack of knowledge about the nature of conferencing as a medium than it is to the nature of the medium itself.

Benefits and Applications of Conferencing

There are several benefits of computer conferencing systems. They are:

- Reduced costs of travel for meetings;
- Ability to include people who could not attend face-to-face meetings;
- Ability to survey opinions of diverse people and have their responses related by specific topics; and
- Ability to extend meetings over both time and distance.

Companies that are extensive users of computer conferencing include Bechtel, Procter & Gamble, Hewlett-Packard, and Digital Equipment. Coca-Cola has also used conferencing very effectively. When it made its fateful mistake of changing its formula and introducing the "New Coke", it used a conferencing system to gather input on the reaction to the change from various locations across the country.

Digital Equipment has used conferencing to help improve group planning in its personnel department. The conferencing system is used to gather input on policy matters from its personnel managers who are located in the field at multiple Digital facilities. Before the conferencing system was used, policy matters were often decided at central headquarters with only minimal input from the field. In fact, the conferencing system, according to Digital employees, has helped reduce a full management layer and has allowed higher level personnel managers to locate at field offices rather than stay centralized at Digital's main headquarters.

The Limitations of Conferencing

The main problem with computer conferencing has little to do with its potential benefits. Instead, the problem with conferencing is related to the difficulty in using it effectively as a medium. People who have used conferencing systems with high expectations of improving their productivity have often been frustrated. The reason, however, has to do with the training provided to users rather than with the inherent nature of the medium itself.

This poses a difficult problem for electronic mail planners. Conferencing has considerable potential to improve group productivity, although it is a difficult medium to use effectively. Should planners try to harness this power for a relatively small group of users or should they spend their limited time in spreading CBMS further throughout their companies, especially as many CBMS now have bulletin boards that provide some of the benefits of conferencing?

In general, the safer course is to forget conferencing until users are far more experienced in using electronic communications and until PC software is available that makes it easier to use conferencing systems, most of which now have line-oriented interfaces. There are many companies, however, that will find applications that can benefit from computer conferencing in areas where there are dispersed groups of people who have a continuing need to hold meetings, but cannot afford the cost or time for travel.

If a company decides to use conferencing, however, it is important to make certain that the base of users understands the nature of the medium so that they will understand the pitfalls of its use. Training users in the specific commands, incidentally, is not sufficient to assure proper usage. Users must also be trained in the art of managing meetings electronically.

PCs and E-Mail

Back in the late 1970s and early 1980s, electronic mail was a hot topic in technology circles, although CBMS were not considered the premier form of electronic mail as they are today. Instead, CBMS were viewed suspiciously as a new technological phenomenon that required serious cost justification before they could be used by companies.

Back in those early days, one of the biggest problems for anyone wanting to use a CBMS was the lack of terminals inside organizations. In early 1981, for example, I wrote an article on CBMS at the request of Auerbach Publishers, Inc., for their research series, *Electronic Office: Management and Technology*. In the section on the limitations of CBMS, I wrote:

> Several factors can currently be considered limitations to the growth of messaging systems—the cost and availability of terminals, the cost and ease of use, possible interconnection of messaging systems, and identification of other users. Terminal costs and ease of use are technology-related factors; external network interconnection and user identification are market-related. The technological factors are unquestionably moving users toward acceptance of personal messaging. . . . Costs for messaging continue to decline. Terminals are likely to be available for less than $500 by the mid-1980s, possibly lowering messaging costs to 15 cents per message on simple systems. . . [1]

Although it is interesting that many of the same problems still exist, such as ease of use and interconnection, and identification of users, the most interesting part of the quote is what it did not say. When the article was written in early 1981, the PC was little more than a technological toy that was not considered a serious office machine. Back then, for example, there were no PCs inside Bell Canada's Business Planning Division, where I then worked. Every plan made for Bell's CBMS service, Envoy 100, was based upon users operating dumb terminals.

It was later that year that the Apple II and the CP/M-based PCs began developing into semi-serious business machines. By early 1982, opinions began changing about PCs around the world, especially when IBM introduced its PC. Almost like a stroke of lightning, electronic mail planners began seeing a new vision, which was articulated in a market research report entitled "Electronic Mail & Personal Computers" that was published in February 1983 by International Resource Development (IRD) of Norwalk, Conn.:

> During the past two years, the personal computer has moved into a central role in both home and business electronics markets. There is no question that the personal computer has arrived as a mass market electronics device and will be sold to millions of home and business users during the coming decade. Since these computers all have the ability to add communications, one of their most powerful impacts is likely to be on the field of electronic mail.
>
> Electronic mail has its roots in three technologies developed in the 1800s—telegraphy, facsimile and telephony. The telex network is already worldwide and has more than 1.5 million users. In addition, electronic mail has been extended to the U.S. Postal Service, which delivers both Mailgram and E-COM messages.
>
> The development of the minicomputer has further benefitted the electronic mail business, allowing for computer-based message systems (CBMS) that give users electronic mailboxes for messages. As significant as these developments have been, however, the personal computer may prove to be the most important development for electronic mail, creating a base of millions of terminals to both send and receive electronic mail.[2]

The Era of Mass Messaging

The PC is ushering in an era of mass messaging in which it will be commonplace for business employees to have an electronic mailbox and to use other computer-aided communications technologies, such as computer conferencing. The era, however, is still in its earliest stages. CBMS and other advanced electronic mail technologies, for example, are still difficult to use for many people who are uncomfortable using a keyboard.

Many PC users also do not like today's public CBMS services, in particular, because of their line editors, command mode of operation, and general screen appearances. Public CBMS services are still heavily influenced by their early days when their planners developed systems to be used by dumb terminals over expensive communication lines. Although better screen-oriented interfaces are possible, they have not been adopted by public service vendors.

Since the PC appeared on the horizon in 1981 and 1982, it has come much further than CBMS and other electronic mail technologies in terms of its user interface. PC software, for example, is well known for its function and cursor-key operations with fast scrolling of text, ring menus (type of menu in Lotus 1-2-3), and what-you-see-is-what-you-get word processing. During the past two years, this has been extended to other techniques such as windows, pull-down and popup menus, desktop accessories, background processing, mice, and other interface devices.

Host to Micro Gap

The advances in microcomputers have created a huge gap between the micros and host computers that are accessed over telecommunication links. Although advanced user interface techniques are flourishing on PCs, host-based CBMS still have a mixture of line-oriented and screen-oriented user interfaces. Even the software packages designed for operation on in-house systems, such as Digital's ALL-IN-1, Hewlett-Packard's Desk-Manager III, and IBM's PROFs, have only acceptable screen-oriented user interfaces that do not have full window support and are not as well developed as interfaces on PCs. The IBM world, furthermore, still has a problem allowing wordwrap with editors.

Wordwrapping is dependent on the machine counting characters as it nears the end of a line of text. As soon as the characters run over the line length, the machine takes all of the characters before the last space and moves them to the next line by sending a carriage return and a line feed. In technical parlance, this is called a "soft" carriage return because it really does not exist in the text. It is supplied by the machine while displaying the text but is not saved with the text file. The ability of microcomputers to provide these "soft" returns in word processors allows the user to keep on typing without entering a "hard" carriage return until the end of a paragraph. This capability is not only a convenience for users, but it is also the heart of the formatting capabilities in word processors, which format on the basis of hard carriage returns that delineate paragraphs.

Because IBM networks only receive the transmission of a full screen when a special "enter" key is pressed on the keyboard, IBM mainframes cannot perform wordwrapping directly. Instead, IBM terminal controllers have an option, called Entry Assist, that provides local wordwrapping capabilities. Not all controllers, however, have Entry Assist installed. Editors on the IBM mainframe, furthermore, must be written to work with Entry Assist.

Packet switching networks also do not recognize the concept of wordwrapping. While the local packet switching nodes provide character echoing, for example, they are not programmed to perform wordwrapping locally. In order to perform wordwrapping over a packet network, it would have to be provided by the host, which would have to echo back characters over the packet network. Although this is possible, it would be very resource-intensive, expensive, and, most likely, slow. Each character, for example, would take up a separate packet as it was echoed back to the PC or terminal, along with instructions to wrap the words that overflowed the column.

Today's popular communications rates of 1,200 and 2,400 bps also make it difficult for hosts to provide sophisticated screen-handling capabilities, such as pop-up or pull-down menus and wordwrapping for text editing. Screen refresh rates are too slow at 1,200 bps to allow such features to be controlled by a remote system with user friendliness. Although modems are moving toward from 9,600 to 19,200 bps, which in a few years may overcome many of the speed limitations, this is small consolation for planners who must deal with today's realities. By the time 9,600 bps modems drop in price to the $100 to $200 range, there will likely be about 10 to 20 million or more 1,200 bps and 2,400 bps modems installed, representing a cost of more than $2 billion to convert to modems with higher speeds.

In terms of the automobile-roadway and retail-store analogy that we have used before, the development of the cars (PCs) is out of phase with the development of the roads (networks). In turn, this makes it difficult for the retail stores (hosts) to meet the needs of their shoppers (end users).

Cost of Electronic Mail Access

Even though there is a wide gap between PCs and host-based CBMS, the PC has still become the catalyst that has initiated the spread of electronic mail. PCs are purchased to run primary application programs such as word processors, spreadsheets, and data base programs. Once this cost is incurred, it is an incremental cost to add the ability to communicate; i.e., the cost of a modem and telecommunications software. During the past five years, this cost has dropped so substantially that it has caused a few million people to make an effort to overcome the limitations of using electronic mail. Figure 10-1 shows how the costs have dropped since 1980 for people to access remote processing services for PCs.

The figure tracks the cost of a 1,200 bps modem and communications software from 1980 through 1986 and then projects the trend line to 1988. The costs, incidentally, do not take bundling and site licensing into consideration, which are two marketing techniques that have been used to lower costs further. Beginning in 1983, for example, it became quite common for telecommunications software to be bundled in with the modem. As an example, Hayes Microcomputer Products (Atlanta, Ga.), the leading vendor of modems for microcomputers, turned its Smartcom II program into one of the market leaders by bundling it with the purchase of its modems.

Figure 10-1. Cost of Electronic Mail Access

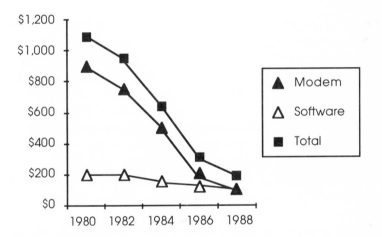

Modem speeds are shifting rapidly toward 2,400 bps as the most popular speed. By 1988, it is likely that 2,400 bps modems will replace 1,200 bps modems on the above price curve. The PC modem market also has some 9,600 bps modems available for prices in the $800 range, although these modems are not always based on international standards, which limits their use to controlled applications. In fact, there are now ultra-fast modems that can operate at speeds up to 18,000 bps for prices in the $1,000 to $1,300 range. Although these modems are cost-effective for specialized, high volume applications, they are too expensive to put on every user's desk.

There are also changes in the quality of the telecommunications software, which are covered in more detail later in this chapter. Telecom software for PCs is now entering its third generation of development, which will have a major impact on the ability of people to use electronic mail systems.

The User Interface Problem

Dropping cost is not the only reason why people have purchased modems. In general, the lack of understanding about communications-related applications has resulted in a lot of hype about the power of using a PC to communicate. Many people who purchased modems and telecom software, for example, expected to enter a new world where important information was at their fingertips and electronic mail was a few keystrokes away. Although the electronic mail capability and information are there (or at least much of the information) and are used by about 1 to 2 million PC users, many of these users have been very disappointed by the difficulty of using online telecommunication services, which extends to every phase of the process, from the log-on procedures to learning the commands for system operations.

The user interface problem is a serious one for electronic mail planners, although not necessarily from the perspective of finding good interfaces to electronic mail systems. There are now several million PCs with modems and a larger number of PCs that can be turned into communication devices for a cost of under $200 apiece. This is the latent potential that analysts have been projecting to explode into almost unprecedented demand for online communications and information access. Although many people expected the explosion in the mid-1980s, what happened was that many users rejected communications because of the unfriendliness of online systems. They did not, however, reject the idea of communications itself. The result is that water is now building against a very rickety dam, with the pressure at unprecedented levels.

Solutions to the user interface problem are now reaching the market, with dozens more under development. This amounts to a flood of high quality user interfaces to online systems. The good news, of course, is that users will have the high quality interfaces, the lack of which until now has contributed greatly to holding back usage. The bad news is that planners will have to deal with the consequences of a new wave of technology. Looked at from another angle, the bottom-up demand that led to an explosion in PC procurement could soon repeat itself in online communications. The major problem facing electronic mail planners is to be ready for the wave.

The purpose of this chapter is to put the issue into perspective so that planners will have as clear a frame of reference as possible about the relationship of PCs to electronic mail. The first step is to explore the functionality of PCs as they relate to electronic mail, which should provide a frame of reference for overall solutions to planning problems. The second step is to explore the problems that will most likely develop when the coming wave of new technology reaches the market. The third step is to explore potential solutions not only to connecting PCs into electronic mail systems, which is the easy part, but to the real impending problem, which is managing the wave of new technology that is about to engulf everyone.

Electronic Mail Functionality

When the enthusiasm is moderated, the PC has one major role as an electronic mail device. It serves as the connecting point into a wide variety of potential electronic mail and information services. PCs can perform this role in three basic ways:

- As a point-to-point electronic-mail system;
- As a workstation to access host services; and
- As an electronic mailbox/user agent.

These three functions are not mutually exclusive. Instead, the functions have a ranked value. The most valuable function is to use the PC as an electronic mailbox and user agent for all types of mail, such as ASCII text files, binary program files, and specially formatted files for applications programs. The second choice is to use PCs as workstations to communicate with central hosts. The least attractive choice is to use PCs in their own point-to-point networks.

Unfortunately, although the functions may have a clear rank in terms of theoretical preference, it is doubtful that PCs are ready today to be used to their maximum value as electronic mail devices, although they are certainly getting closer. Limitations on the technology necessitate less attractive choices. The key point for planners is to make the short-term compromises in such a way that they do not put barriers in the way of long-term development.

PC as a Point-to-Point Mail Device

The PC not only serves as a latent communications device to send short messages, but it also creates the need to send the files created through its main uses: word processing, financial planning, data base management, and program development. These files, however, have formatting codes or are binary programs that must be transferred without errors. Special file transfer protocols, such as Xmodem and Kermit, were quickly developed to allow these files to be transferred between PCs without errors. The need and ability to transfer files has led to a number of electronic mail applications for PCs in the areas of transferring computer programs amongst remote programming teams and in sending reports, documents, and other data that are prepared on PCs from field offices to central headquarters. There are numerous companies, especially smaller ones, that have already set up very successful point-to-point networks and a larger number that are planning such networks today.

The early success in setting up effective point-to-point PC networks for file transfers of important information has led to the view that PCs can be set up in their own networks without the need for any central host providing store-and-forward control. There are some people, for example, who believe that PC networks will make CBMS obsolete. Although point-to-point networks are seductive because they can be set up easily and do not require extensive training to operate, they have built-in limits that planners must keep in mind, especially if growth is anticipated.

When point-to-point networks are first set up, volumes are typically low, with a few files per week being transferred. This makes it easy for users to call each other up and set up the file transfers manually. As volume grows, however, the senders start finding it harder to reach someone to set up the transfer, which necessitates many telephone calls just to get one file sent. As volume increases further, recipients start resenting that their day is disrupted to set up such transfers. At this point, the company should start thinking about automating its point-to-point network, which can be accomplished using intelligent buffered modems and dedicated phone lines.

If the company has a PBX without direct inward dialing (the ability to reach the extension with a direct call), for example, it must then install an outside telephone line on each PC on the network, which costs $30 per month per PC. It must also add buffered modems with auto-file transfer capabilities to solve the telephone tag and disruption problems. These devices are available from several companies on the market, including Hayes, Prometheus Products, and Incomnet.

While these costs can probably be justified, a point-to-point network may be shortsighted, regardless of its apparent effectiveness. Marshall McLuhan became famous for a chapter in his book *Understanding Media* entitled, "The Medium is the Message". McLuhan's main point was that each communications medium has a self-governing limitation on its applications. "The 'message' of any medium or technology," he said, "is the change of scale or pace or pattern that it introduces into human affairs."[3]

This "change of scale or pace or pattern" may be the biggest problem with any point-to-point electronic mail network, whether it be based on telex, teletex, facsimile, or PCs. Although point-to-point networks may be cost-effective for delivering small volumes of information, they cannot be extended to other applications that may be far more important.

Consider the company that has a point-to-point PC network to transfer a few reports between a small number of locations weekly. When the company is satisfied with its network, it may never consider that a different medium can not only meet its need for file transfer but also open the door to even more powerful applications, such as planning the delivery of new products, handling customer service problems, or discussing long-term finance and other strategic issues. Although a point-to-point network may work well for transferring weekly reports, it cannot be used for advanced group planning activities, and it may inhibit its users from even considering such possibilities.

Readers, incidentally, should not take this to mean that point-to-point networks are inherently shortsighted. There is a strong role for point-to-point networks that provide forced delivery of PC-based information, particularly since intelligent buffered modems are now available that can automate the operation of the networks. These modems handle all of the delivery operations independently from the PC, so that they can operate if the PC is being used for another task or even if the PC is not turned on.

These products, which are priced from $70 to $800 depending upon capabilities, open up new options for developing electronic mail applications, particularly those that are local and do not incur long distance communication charges. To give a few examples, medical laboratories can use this type of product to deliver lab reports to doctor's offices, eliminating the need for expensive courier services or the slow regular mails. Small retail companies with several branches can set up a network to communicate price changes, orders, sales, payroll information, inventory, and other data. A Real Estate listing service can send up-to-the-minute listings to brokers, instead of requiring them to check with a central service. Lawyers with several key clients can set up a private network to exchange legal documents. In short, intelligent buffered modems, if used creatively, can become a powerful tool for local electronic mail.

PC as a Workstation

PCs make excellent workstations when communicating to remote host computers. In fact, they now go far beyond what most "dumb" or "intelligent" terminals have so far accomplished. Nevertheless, most PC communications software provides users with a mirror into the host computer's environment, which is at the heart of the user interface problem. Since the PC was developed, there have been two generations of advances in telecommunication terminal software, with a third just reaching the market. The generations are roughly equivalent to the advances in PC hardware, which has opened the door to advanced software. The generations are:

- 8-bit PCs, 16K RAM chips, 300 bps modems and floppy disks;
- 16-bit PCs, 64K RAM chips, 1,200 bps modems and 5-10M byte hard disks; and

- 32-bit PCs, 256K-1M RAM chips, chip-based 2,400 bps modems, and 20-40M byte hard disks, or network servers, for disk storage.

As the old saying goes, "Three is a charm." The first two electronic mail generations for PCs resulted in communications software with intelligent terminal emulation, limited communications programming languages, and built-in editors (in the advanced packages). The first generation is most epitomized by two packages— Crosstalk from Microstuf (Norcross, Ga.) and Smartcom II from Hayes Microcomputer Products. To give a brief description, when these packages were first introduced, they provided solid telecom emulation of dumb terminals, the ability to program basic auto-log-in routines that automatically called a network and entered the information required to log on to a host service successfully, and the ability to transfer binary files via file transfer protocols such as Xmodem and Kermit. As the second generation developed, Smartcom and Crosstalk added intelligent terminal emulation of terminals such as Digital's VT-100, the ability to extend their auto-log-in routines to perform limited branching functions, and the ability to call an application program from within the telecom package.

Other second generation packages have gone even further. These packages have all of the above but have added features such as built-in editors, more extensive programming languages, and the ability to run resident as a pop-up program; they can, therefore, be called from within another PC application program. Examples of such second generation packages are Around from Teal Communications (Vancouver, B.C.) and Get! from Cygnet Technologies (Sunnyvale, Calif.). In general, second generation packages automate connection to the host computers and have some beneficial extras, such as the ability to use built-in editors, but they do not solve the user interface problem. A user still must learn the host-based mail systems and interact at slow speeds in comparison to the speeds of a PC application program.

The third generation of software, which is now coming onto the market, is developing in two directions. The CBMS providers have taken one direction by supplying their own customized mail packages that allow users to operate offline for most of their reading, writing, and filing operations. Examples of these packages include Lotus Express and Desktop Express from MCI Mail, PCTelemail from Telemail, Re:Source from The Source, Upfront from Dialcom, and Transend PC, which is used by Geisco's Quik-Comm and Computer Science Corp.'s Notice.

Third-party software developers are taking the other direction by providing sophisticated programming languages that can be used to build complete front ends, including the user interface, an editor and support for advanced interactive protocols, such as X.PC, which allows up to 15 inter-active sessions to be held simultaneously in different windows. These pack-ages include Access from Microsoft (Bellevue, Wash.), BackComm from LaSalle Micro (Schaumburg, Ill.) and Crosstalk Mark IV from Microstuf. The purpose of this book, however, is to explore the strategic implication of these packages, not compare how they operate.

PC as Mailbox and UA

The third generation packages that are just reaching the market will move the PC from a simple workstation into the realm of mailbox and user agent. The programmable third generation software packages, for example, have features such as:

- High-level programming languages that can be programmed to emu-late the online mail environment of numerous hosts so that users may operate almost entirely offline;
- Ability to integrate popular word processors as their editors;
- Full residency with other PC applications in a multi-tasking, window-ing environment; and
- AI techniques to overcome initial log-on problems if they occur.

The third generation packages will have a profound impact on the ease of use of electronic mail systems as well as on the approach that planners take to solve their communication problems. A few years ago, for example, electronic mail had these basic problems associated with usage:

- Cost and availability of terminals;
- Cost of transmitting mail;
- Ease of use of host systems;
- Interconnection of systems; and
- Identification of other users.

Generation 1 of PCs and of their associated modems and telecommunica-tions software addressed the first issue, which is the cost and availability of terminals. Generation 2 lowered costs further and began to address the ease-of-use problem and cost of transmitting the mail. Generation 3 will lower costs still further but will have an even greater impact on the ease of use of electronic mail systems and will also begin to address the issues of interconnection and identification of other users.

The key to the third generation is software that allows users to perform almost all their electronic mail tasks while they are offline, which shifts the user interface from line-oriented editors and simple scrolling to PC-type interfaces with multiple windows and full-screen editors. The PC handles tasks such as calling the host mail systems in background, pulling the mail from the host's inbox, storing it on the PC, notifying the user, and then presenting the mail while the user is offline. Users read the messages offline, file them locally on their hard disks (or a network server), and use their regular word processor or an easy-to-use full-screen editor to create any new mail or reply/forward existing mail.

A good example of a third generation package is Desktop Express, which allows Apple Macintosh users to operate on MCI Mail. Desktop Express uses icons for the various mailboxes. By clicking with the Macintosh's mouse, users can enter their various mailboxes. The package, which supports the MNP interactive error correction protocol from Microcom, also has a built-in editor and can attach binary and formatted files for error-free transmission to MCI Mail. Recipients with Desktop Express packages can receive the files. In addition, word processing files can be printed out for delivery exactly as they would have printed out locally.

In short, the third generation packages go a long way toward solving the ease-of-use problems associated with e-mail systems by bringing most of the mail environment into the PC itself. As a by-product of this process, if the third generation packages run in a multi-tasking environment, users will not have to worry about checking their mailboxes regularly because their PCs will do it for them, which will go a long way toward solving the growing problem of users who do not check their mailboxes regularly.

Third generation packages will not stop there in their impact. Although the first packages to reach the market have dealt largely with user interface issues, the leading edge packages will start to address interconnection and identification of users by functioning as user agents within popular networking environments, such as SNADS, Digital's MAILbus, and the X.400 international message transfer standard. Already, for example, there are X.400-based software and user agents on the market designed to run on packet switching networks.

As significant as X.400 interconnection will be, however, this may not be the most important impact of the third generation packages developed by independent software companies. These packages can provide electronic mail planners with a long-term solution to the growing chaos in communications by serving as general development programs for multiple applications. One of the implications of third generation software is that each specific host will require a customized front end package. As it is unlikely that companies will only use one program for all of their communication applications, this will mean that users will require a separate PC-based front end program for each host-based application. As a company may have numerous host-based programs, it may be able to standardize on one PC front end package to build a common interface to multiple applications, which will greatly ease the problem of introducing new applications into the organization.

Today's PC Communications World

To put it mildly, the world of PC-based communications is in a state of flux (some may call it chaos). There are already more than 200 micro-to-mainframe software programs and 100 general telecommunications packages on the market. There is also a strong developing trend for highly specialized communications software, such as programs that transfer Lotus 1-2-3 files from PCs to mainframes and then integrate the files with specific mainframe data base programs or programs that allow PC interaction with mail systems, such as Desktop Express, Lotus Express, and PCTelemail.

The present situation is literally a planner's nightmare. Many companies, for example, have just spent months choosing one or two "standard" PC-based communications packages and negotiating site licenses, with the result that they now have "standard" software that is already obsolete. How can a planner cope with an environment where the technology moves faster than the ability to plan for its implementation? There just does not seem to be a way to win.

Heart of a New Generation

To better understand the nature of the problem facing electronic mail planners, consider the steps required to develop a specialized electronic mail application program designed to overcome the limitations imposed by the roadways, such as logging on through a maze of strange prompts, interacting in line mode, and learning a new set of commands to control the host's electronic mail program and the line editor. Every interaction between the PC and the host must be translated from the host's line orientation into the PC's screen-oriented interface. Furthermore, for the program to work properly, it must take error situations into consideration, otherwise the program will bomb out as soon as it encounters an unexpected situation.

This complex interaction is a necessity and will remain so until the roadways catch up to the ability of PCs to present information to users. During the past two years, the highly specialized third generation programs designed to overcome these limitations have been built from scratch on an application-by-application basis.

The heart of the independent third generation communications programs is their underlying languages that can be used to build many different applications with the same basic interface. The programs are really a set of tools that give application developers a way to allow a PC to be integrated into a host communication program without having to build the front end program from scratch. Such tools include:

- A window where commands can be chosen from a menu (either pull-down, pop-up or ring (e.g., Lotus 1-2-3);
- A window where a text editor or word processor can be inserted to allow messages or files from a PC program to be created;
- A programming language that not only handles basic communication routines but also is rich enough to create complete metaphors such as handling an inbox-outbox on a desktop or attending an electronic meeting;
- The ability to receive commands from the host under program control as well as from the user at the keyboard; and
- File transfer routines that can take a designated file and send it to the host with error detection and correction.

The Forest Through the Trees

The main goal for electronic mail planners today is to develop a strategy that lets them see the forest of communications through the trees of specialized front ends that are now engulfing the market. Companies have two choices:

- They can use the specialized software on a case-by-case basis, which will result in a barrage of different programs, each of which does the job well, but with a different interface; or
- They can take the lead and find a software package that they can program to interface to almost any type of host system.

Although it is likely that most companies will want to take advantage of custom third generation programs to meet immediate needs, over the long term it is equally advisable to look for an independent third generation program that can be used internally to create multiple applications with a consistent user interface.

PCs, Communication Roadways, and E-Mail

The roadways are the weak link that causes problems in the relationship between PCs and host computers. As the link becomes stronger, the user interface problems will tend to melt away. Already for example, LANs that operate at high speeds are beginning to proliferate, with the result being that PCs can communicate over these networks as if they were communicating internally to their own disk drives.

These high speed LANs are the first step in a long-term rebuilding of our communication roadways. Although most of them now operate within a single department, there is already a movement in many companies toward interconnecting multiple LANs within a building and/or campus. Advanced PBXs that operate at speeds of 56,000 bps are already on the market, and the even more advanced ISDN (Integrated Services Digital Network) switches are entering their beta testing phase, which gives organizations another high speed roadway to compete with LANs. Ultimately, these high speeds will be extended to long distance links.

Impact of LANs and Advanced PBXs

LANs and advanced PBXs will change the PC-to-host equations for electronic mail by:

- Allowing hosts to run more sophisticated software;
- Allowing companies to put electronic mail software on small, dedicated hosts, rather than on large minis or mainframes that run multiple applications; and
- Providing an environment where small hosts can be networked together to distribute messages throughout an organization.

Already most LANs have electronic mail packages available for their users, although these packages are only now winning awards for sophistication. The leading independent mail packages for IBM PC-based LANs are cc:Mail from PCC Systems (Menlo Park, Calif.) and Network Courier from Consumer Software (Vancouver, B.C.). A number of LAN vendors, such as Banyon (Westboro, Mass.), 3COM (Sunnyvale, Calif.), and Novell (Orem, Utah) also have good mail packages. As this software matures further, it will allow small electronic mail hosts in multiple departments within an organization to be networked together, as well as to outside networks such as public CBMS and private mail systems such as Digital's ALL-IN-1 and IBM's PROFs, telex, and facsimile. Assuming that the roadways develop as envisioned, electronic mail will be driven by networked systems on the departmental or buildingwide level, depending upon the roadway.

Today's Reality and Planning Cycles

Electronic mail seems headed toward networked, departmental systems for a significant portion of users within corporations. Moving from today's relatively centralized environment to a fully decentralized network is very difficult, especially if planners want to meet immediate user needs within the context of a long-term plan.

This poses a major planning problem within organizations, especially when one considers the speed at which new technology is developing. Many planning cycles are far longer than technological developments, which results in decisions to use products that are obsolete when they are finally spread throughout the company. PCs, of course, add more fuel to the fire because they are driving out the need to transfer binary and formatted files as well as ASCII text.

To give just one example of what planners face today, many departments are requesting small LANs with from 5 to 20 users, all of whom will be given electronic mail on the LAN. At the same time, the company may have an electronic mail system on a company mainframe that operates over a leased line network. If the LAN has a gateway facility that allows users to share modems to access the central mail system, this certainly eases the problem. But even then, it gives users two mailboxes, each of which has a different set of commands and interfaces, which may result in users not checking the corporate mailbox. Furthermore, this does nothing to address the problem of transferring binary and formatted files from the LAN mail environments to the corporate mail system, communicating directly with other LANs, or allocating funds in an environment with limited resources.

Summary

The problems that face electronic mail planners cannot be solved without careful strategic planning. There are too many competing technologies in hosts, networks, and PCs that are out of phase with each other. Planners must weigh long-term goals against short-term gains when evaluating where to allocate limited resources.

There are two important problems that must be solved to foster the development of a successful electronic mail system. The first is the roadway problem, so that proper electronic mail networks can develop. Evolving from a few central systems and some errant LANs into a true network requires a quantum leap in architectural concepts. Because other applications, such as electronic business forms and document transfer are also involved, planning an electronic mail network involves completely rethinking today's systems. This, of course, will take time and will not meet immediate user needs. Planners, however, can start from the bottom up and, at the least, make sure that electronic mail software running on LANs will be compatible with any resulting network.

The second is the user interface problem of connecting PCs to electronic mail and other host-based services, such as data bases. This problem can be addressed directly by electronic mail planners with very rapid results by identifying custom third generation packages that can meet immediate needs, as well as independent packages that can serve as the basis for building a common interface to multiple applications and hosts. As the PC is the entry point for electronic mail regardless of how the network is organized, good interface software has value from both short- and long-term prospectives, which makes it one of the most important priorities today for an electronic mail planner.

Voice Mail

In the late 1950s, some enterprising engineers integrated a low cost tape recorder with a telephone to develop the simplest electronic mail device on the market—the telephone answering machine. Although many readers, especially those who are enamored of the fancy technology that often sits beneath electronic mail systems, might recoil at the thought that a lowly answering machine is an electronic mail device, it nevertheless fits the definition perfectly by allowing people to leave non-interactive messages for other people.

The answering machine, of course, has never been recognized as a serious electronic mail device and, instead, has been treated as a specialized consumer and business electronics product. It was, however, the beginning of an entirely new branch of the electronic mail family—voice mail. Like other electronic mail technologies, voice mail has come to use the computer as its quarterback; so, when people talk about voice mail today, they usually refer to computer-based voice mail systems that are set up to process voice messages rather than text messages.

Development of Voice Mail

Although academic researchers were responsible for the development of text-based CBMS, voice mail was developed by researchers in the telephone and commercial computer industries. AT&T, for example, developed a voice mail system, the IAESS voice storage system, to provide voice mailboxes to telephone subscribers. Unfortunately, users were never able to experience the system because of regulatory issues. In 1968, AT&T filed with the FCC to offer the service first via Bell Telephone Co. of Pennsylvania. Because of Computer Inquiry II, however, which separated value-added from basic services, the filing was denied and AT&T put voice mail on its back burner, although it did not stop product development.

In 1974, an R&D startup company called Sudbury Systems, Inc. (Sudbury, Mass.) developed a technique for digitizing voices and storing them in electronic mailboxes and entered the market by focusing on the medical industry. In 1978, ECS Telecommunications, Inc. (Richardson, Tex.) was started by well known telecommunications entrepreneur Gordon Matthews.[1] ECS developed the first general-purpose, commercial voice mail system called the VMX (Voice Mail Exchange) and also filed for a patent on the voice mail digitization process in November 1979, which was granted in February 1983 as U.S. Patent #4,371,752. ECS delivered its first machine in May 1980 to 3M Corp. and now has about 175 to 200 systems installed worldwide, making it the leader in the industry.

During the same period that Sudbury was doing its research, engineers from IBM were also experimenting with digitizing voice and storing it in a mailbox system. IBM entered the market in 1981 with its Audio Distribution System (ADS), which was based on the Series/1 minicomputer. Shortly afterwards PBX-maker Rolm and word processing vendor Wang also jumped into the market with voice mail systems. Although each system had slightly differing features, they were all basically the same. Each one had a simple scheme to allow users to control the voice mail system from a touch-tone telephone (or touch-tone pad) to perform the functions of sending and receiving messages.

Voice Mail's Disappointing Performance

Although text-based CBMS were viewed with suspicion by industry analysts when they were first developed, voice mail systems were tagged almost immediately as one of the hot technologies of the 1980s. Market analysts, for example, expected that AT&T would enter the market with a heavy investment and that the overall market would grow into a multibillion dollar industry by the late 1980s or early 1990s.[2]

Voice mail's expected boom has not yet occurred. AT&T, for example, did not enter the market until 1985 and did so with a relative whimper rather than with a major investment. Other companies in the market have experienced a far higher level of resistance from users than anticipated. The result has been a market fizzle in comparison to expectations, although voice mail systems have evolved into a respectable business. There are now about 1,500 to 2,000 voice mail systems installed in companies in North America, with most installations in Fortune 500-type corporations. In terms of total users, there are about 500,000 to 750,000. The capital investment to acquire these systems is in the range of $150 to $200 million (roughly $200 to $300 per user).

Many analysts, still expect that voice mail systems will take off in the market, and there are increasing signs that voice mail systems, in fact, are ready to boom. The reasons why sales of voice mail systems have not materialized as expected are probably related to:

• The difficulty of establishing a knowledgeable distribution channel;

- Scarce capital-investment dollars;
- Overoptimism about user resistance to change; and
- Limitation of the medium.

The Distribution Channel

Both vendors and users are impacted by distribution channels. For any product to succeed, for example, it must have a means of placing it before potential users, who then must give it a fair hearing and be ready to purchase it. Voice mail systems are only now developing such a channel. Voice mail systems, for example, are sold primarily through telecommunication distribution channels, which are very conservative and technically oriented. Most telecommunications managers, for example, are focused on keeping telephone costs as low as possible and make most of their planning decisions based on engineering-related issues, such as traffic loads, line quality, and hardware quality. Although telecommunications managers have done a superb job in bringing high quality telephone service to their organizations, they have traditionally had little experience or incentive to procure products that improve productivity in specific user departments.

This means that voice mail has been a complex sale that required that the salesperson either motivate the telecommunications manager to bring in the heads of different departments so that voice mail could be properly evaluated, or bypass the telecommunications manager and go directly to end user departments. Many companies, however, are not organized to make either of these alternatives easy for a salesperson, with the result that voice mail has gone through a lengthy period of establishing trial systems to have its usage accepted as a standard telecommunications product.

The Capital Investment Issue

Even when voice mail gets a good hearing by potential users, it still has one final hurdle to overcome— the capital investment. Most electronic mail purchases are not yet major capital investments. Modems and telecommunications software, for example, are often purchased piecemeal and charged to each department's budget, which allows procurements to be hidden in departmental budgets. Although a company may spend $300,000 or more on such products, there is no central control over their procurement, which allows purchasing to be driven by bottom-up demand. Facsimile, telex, and even CBMS software are examples of this bottoms-up procurement.

As an example, I remember interviewing a telecommunications manager who told the story of how he thought that there were only 15 facsimile machines in his organization. The manager, however, said that he commissioned a company inventory of telecommunications equipment and discovered that the company had more than 100 fax machines, most of which were rented by separate departments on their own. This type of story is not rare. Well known industry consultant Amy Wohl, for example, once told the same story, except that she was talking with an MIS director who thought that there were only 50 or so PCs in his organization. After an inventory, however, it turned out there were more than 500.

To see how this bottoms up purchasing phenomenon can occur, CBMS software is normally purchased independent of hardware and can be expensed as part of the user's departmental budget. Even programs such as IBM's PROFs and Applied Data Research's eMail, which are among the most expensive host-based programs in the industry (in the $30,000 to $40,000 range), are small purchases in comparison to other products that are run on mainframes. More importantly, they can easily be added to the MIS department's budget as an expense; thus, the decision remains within one department and does not require any capital investment review.

An in-house voice mail system, however, requires a hardware purchase that can be 20 to 40 percent as costly as the original telephone system (most voice mail systems are integrated with the company's PBX). More importantly, the purchase is often large enough that it requires a capital investment review where it competes against other potential capital investments. Given the inherent difficulty of cost justifying any type of electronic mail product, the competition with other capital projects poses yet another barrier to sales.

Resistance to Change

Although voice mail systems are easier to use than text-based systems, there is still considerable user resistance to voice mail. To prove this, buy a telephone answering machine and use it for a few weeks. The chances are high that close to one half of the callers will not leave messages because they do not like to talk to machines. Despite the best attempts of voice mail vendors to distinguish voice mail from answering machines, they have not yet found a way to overcome the basic problem of people not wanting to talk to machines. This can only be solved by time and exposure to a new medium. In sum, although voice mail is growing steadily and has some clearly beneficial uses, it has a number of barriers that have held back its widespread adoption.

Limitation of the Medium

Voice mail is limited by the medium of voice, which is highly effective in exchanging large volumes of information in face-to-face conversations but not particularly effective for a store-and-forward medium, except for short messages. A text-based CBMS, for example, can be used to send messages of a few words or a document that is a few dozen pages. Few people, however, can deliver long voice messages into a machine effectively, and even fewer can listen to long messages. Although voice mail advocates, for example, initially believed that voice mail could replace the need for text-based CBMS, this will never happen because of the need to send long documents and forms. The spread of PCs, furthermore, has increased the need for text-based mail systems because original material is often captured directly in a computer format. If anything, voice mail will become a subset of an integrated message system that handles both text and voice, rather than text mail being outdated by voice mail.

Types of Voice Mail Systems

There are two types of voice mail systems that can be procured: the stand-alone systems or the ones integrated with a PBX. Stand-alone voice mail systems function analogously to CBMS and are operated as either public or in-house timesharing systems; integrated systems operate as general voice mail systems and also serve as telephone answering machines.

Telephone Answering Machine Features

Systems that are integrated with PBXs not only handle messages amongst those with mailboxes but also function as answering machines for users with mailboxes. These integrated systems are connected to telephone extensions on the PBX. The user with a voice mailbox uses the PBX's call forwarding feature to direct calls to the voice mail system when the user wants to invoke the answering machine capability. When a call is placed to the user, it is forwarded to the voice mail system, which answers with either a general message or with the user's personal voice, depending upon the degree of integration.

In a simple PBX integration, the voice mail system is set up as a blind extension on the PBX and answers with a general message that instructs the caller to punch in the user's extension in order to leave a message. In a full PBX integration, the voice mail system recognizes special codes that are sent by the PBX to identify the extension from where the call was forwarded. The voice mail system then knows the user who is being called and plays the user's specially recorded message. As might be expected, fully integrated voice mail systems are now the most popular on the market.

General Voice Mail Features

Voice mail systems have features that are almost identical to basic CBMS when used by people with full IDs. Each user has an inbox of messages with headers that include the caller's name and the time and date the call was placed. The recipient can scan the calls in the inbox; specify the order in which calls are listened to; and then reply to, forward, save, or delete each message. Most voice mail systems, furthermore, have features such as address lists, which allow one call to be automatically sent to multiple recipients.

Voice Mail User Interface

The voice mail system's user interface is based on a touch-tone telephone or pad. The voice mail session itself is controlled by the CBMS, which talks to its users in a synthesized voice and provides the user with a verbal menu that identifies the number of choices at each step in the session. Commands themselves are usually single numbers selected from the voice menu and are often concluded by either the asterisk (*) or pound sign (#) that are on all telephone keypads.

A Voice Mail Session

To log on to a mail system, for example, the system asks the user to enter a numeric ID, which is often the user's telephone extension, followed by #. The system then asks users to enter a password, which is again concluded with #. The good systems will also instruct the user that help is available at any point via some simple technique, such as pressing * and H (number 4). (The commands vary from system to system.)

After logging on, the system tells the user whether or not there are any new messages and then gives a menu of simple choices, such as *press 1 to receive messages, press 2 to create a message, press 3 to change your personal greeting, press 4 for other choices.* When the user presses 1, the system reads the scan line for the first message and directs him or her to *press 0 to listen to the message, press * D to delete the message, press # to skip to the next header.* Users do not have to wait for the instructions from the system, incidentally, but can enter these commands at any time, which allows new users to learn the system as they go through a session but without holding back experienced users.

After a message has been played, the user is instructed to *press 1 to respond to the message, press 2 to forward the message, press * D to delete the message, press # to move to the next message.* If the user presses 1, the system instructs the user to *please reply to the message at the tone, press # when you have finished.* If the user presses 2 (forwarding the message), the system would prompt *please enter the ID of the recipient and end with #.* After entering the ID, the system would prompt the user to enter the message.

To create a message, the user is prompted to enter the ID of the recipient. After entering an ID, the system prompts *press 1 to enter the message, press 2 to enter another recipient, press * D to stop creating the message.* In this way, the user can address the message to multiple recipients. There are, incidentally, two variations of addressing. Although most systems require their users to have numeric IDs, IBM and AT&T use an algorithm that allows users to type in the physical names of users by using the alphabetic letters on the touch-tone pad. The system itself looks for all of the various permutations when a number (which represents three letters) is pressed and then determines the addressee by a process of elimination. When there are multiple people identified, the system reads off the name of each person in a menu.

Which method is better? The most likely answer is neither. Numeric IDs are easy to use because people normally enter numbers on the keypad, but harder to remember. Alphabetic names are easier to remember, but harder to use.

One of the interesting parts of a voice mail system is that messages can be edited or, at a minimum, reviewed before they are sent. After the message itself is entered, the system prompts *press 1 to send the message, press 2 to review the message, press 3 to recreate the message, press * D to delete the message.* Some systems have developed complex algorithms that allow the user to insert or delete parts of the message. Most users, however, prefer to begin a message from scratch and do not use the editing features, which are cumbersome.

Voice Mail Applications

Voice mail systems are very simple to use because of the combination of verbal prompting and menu operation from the telephone keypad. Their capacity, however, is very limited because of the limitations of voice as a stored medium. People need visual feedback to handle long messages. This reduces a voice mail system's effectiveness to fairly short messages, which limits its viability. In general, the major reasons for using voice mail are:

- Eliminating telephone tag;
- Broadcasting messages to a group, which takes considerably less time than calling each person individually; and
- Using the system to lower the cost of answering telephones within the organization.

Although voice mail can be used as a generic tool for all communications within an organization, its price has normally caused usage to migrate to applications where telephone tag and broadcasting messages have the greatest impact on the organization. Such applications include communications within the company's sales organization and communication between the organization and key suppliers.

To give one example, a sales manager may often make 10 to 15 calls each day to talk with members of the sales force to repeat a similar message. Voice mail is used to broadcast one message to the sales force, which can save 20 to 30 telephone calls (when telephone tag is included). Another application is between a salesperson and key customers, especially in commodity-oriented businesses with constant reorders. The salesperson may be constantly on the road and difficult to reach. By using voice mail and checking the mailbox every hour, no customer is ever more than an hour or so away from reaching the salesperson, which is an important means of improving customer service.

Cost Justification and Cross Elasticities

Voice mail systems are cost justified based on two components: its use as an answering machine and its use as a mailbox system for regular users. In general, voice mail ranks much higher as a general answering machine than as a closed CBMS between users because of the limited number of messages that require broadcast by the voice mail system. Such messages are normally sent via paper memos and are only suitable for a voice mail system if they are short enough not to require the user to deliver a soliloquy.

This can be tested by saving the paper memos that circulate in an office and by imagining how they would sound if delivered via voice mail. It must be remembered that most people are far more comfortable and effective in two-way conversations than they are in delivering speeches or listening to a machine.

Finally, when voice mail is used to replace telephone conversations, the medium loses its interactive nature; so, although it may lower costs and save the manager time, it also reduces feedback. A sales manager who uses voice mail to broadcast a message to a sales force, for example, may find that an audio teleconference is a better alternative for many situations.

Justification Through Use as an Answering Machine

Vendors of voice mail systems have approached cost justification from different angles. Rolm, for example, has focused on justifying its mail system, called Phonemail, as an answering machine and provides potential purchasers with a chart, an adapted version of which is shown in Table 11-1.[3]

As can be seen, Rolm concludes that voice mail is roughly 50 to 80 percent less expensive per month than using a message center and from 80 to 93 percent less expensive than having a group secretary who answers telephones. Rolm is basing its assumptions on a $70,000 voice mail system that is depreciated over 5 years and provides support for 125 people ($20 per month per user) or a $185,000 system that supports 800 people ($7 per month per user). It is compared to 30 percent of the time for a $20,000 per year secretary (fully burdened costs) who supports the telephones for 5 people, and 1 full-time person ($20,000 per year) in a message center that provides support for 50 people.

Although voice mail is clearly cost-effective when it is used as an answering machine (provided that companies are willing to amortize the savings over five years), it comes at a cost that has a subjective weight— the value of a person answering the telephone. This reaches the heart of one of the major problems of cost justifying any electronic mail system. It is rare that electronic mail can be justified in a direct apples-to-apples cost comparison.

Justification as a Value-Added System

Wang has taken a different approach to cost justification; it has circulated a case study performed by one of its users— an unidentified Midwestern furniture manufacturer.[4]

The system was installed in 1983 and was studied via questionnaires administered to 206 users before and after the installation. Of the 206 people, 16 were executives, 92 managers, 64 professionals, 8 secretaries, and 26 sales people. In the pre-installation study, users estimated that they were involved in 24 telephone calls per day on average. After the study, users estimated that they handled only 21 calls per day. Telephone messages, furthermore, dropped from 14 to 9 per day, and the telephone tag cycle dropped 33 percent.

Another important finding was that receivers in the pre-installation study estimated that 77 percent of their calls did not have enough information for them to act on a request and send back a return, whereas receivers said that 75 percent of the messages received on the voice mail system had sufficient information. Furthermore, the users estimated that the overall response time for handling voice mail messages was considerably faster than without it.

As an example, 29 percent estimated that their response time cycles improved by 1 to 3 hours, 34 percent estimated that the cycle improved by 4 to 6 hours, 17 percent estimated that the cycle improved by 7 to 9 hours, and 20 percent estimated that the cycle improved by more than 10 hours. In all, 90 percent of the users said they believed that voice mail improved their productivity.

Table 11-1. Cost Comparison of Voice Mail
as a Telephone Answering Service

	Phonemail	Message Center	Group Secretary
Number of hours during the the day when callers can leave messages or users can get their messages	24 hrs.	9-12 hrs.	8-9 hrs.
Delay between time message is left by caller and time message is received	no delay	1-4 hrs.	short delay
Accessibility of messages from various locations	from any touch-tone telephone	from one location	accessible at or near secretary's desk
Cost per month per user	$7-$20	$40	$100

Evaluating the Justifications

In general, users should beware of cost justifications performed or released by vendors. Neither the Rolm nor Wang justifications, for example, had any information about the negatives of using voice mail versus conventional media, which means that they were putting their best foot forward. The Wang study particularly should be viewed with caution because it was based on user perceptions, not on an actual analysis of traffic. How important can this be? Canadian consulting firm Trigon Systems Group (now a part of DMR Group Inc.) once performed a perception versus actuality study of how employees in a department of a large bank spent their time. In the study of perceptions, the employees estimated that they spent 62 percent of their time in internal communications and 38 percent communicating with customers. In the actual analysis, the employees turned out to spend 92 percent of their time in internal communications—a variance of 30 percent.

The Wang study also did not estimate the cost benefit of the improved telephone communications; so, although users perceived an improvement, they did not know whether it was worth the extra costs. This is another element inherent in cost justifying electronic mail (as well as many other new office technologies). Although it is commonplace to have the new technology perceived as improving productivity, there are few studies that yield hard dollar justifications of the costs.

Readers should not take these comments to mean that voice mail is not cost justified. The very opposite is probably the case. The Wang and Rolm studies give planners some excellent insight into its potential benefits and justifications. The Rolm study, in particular, provides surprising cost advantages, and the Wang study shows clearly how voice mail is perceived to improve internal telephone communications. Cost justification, however, is a very difficult and imprecise science that requires careful thought before being applied, lest the planner come up with some very wrong answers.

Voice Mail Architecture

Voice mail is a rapidly developing technology in which prices have been dropping at an astonishing rate. The first voice mail systems introduced in 1980 to 1981, for example, had price tickets from about $100,000 to $300,000 and were designed to support from 100 to 3,000 users, which was a variance of from $1,000 to $100 per user— the catch being that the best cost per user ratios were available only on giant systems that were never installed.

The systems themselves consist of some type of computer, an analog-to-digital voice processing subsystem, disk storage, and software to provide the mailbox and answering machine environment. The two key elements in the process are the voice digitization rate and the amount of storage that is available. For example, a letter that takes 1.25 minutes to read can be stored in 1.6K bytes of disk when stored in text form but requires 300K bytes when stored as a digitized voice message using a 32K bps digitization rate. As can be seen, a voice mail system's major cost component is disk space.

Digitization Rates

When voice mail systems were first developed, one of the biggest secrets was the digitization rate that was used. AT&T, for example, uses a digitization rate of 64K bps in its pulse-code modulated (PCM) digital communication trunks. VMX uses a 32K bps digitization rate, which has been adopted by most of the vendors in the industry. The 32K bps rate, in theory, is about the lowest that engineers can go and still retain the original quality of each individual's voice unless extremely sophisticated data compression techniques are used. Thus, most voice mail systems use 32K bps, although a few advanced systems use a rate of 16K bps or lower and claim good quality.

Impact on Storage and Usage

The high digitization rate means that voice mail systems require huge amounts of memory to store their messages. In practice, this means that most voice mail systems cannot be used for long-term storage of messages by each user. Instead, the systems are designed with the idea that users release their messages from their inbox after they have been heard. A beginning system, for example, typically can support 4 simultaneous callers (4 ports), has storage for a total of 6 hours, and can support up to 40 users, which gives each user storage of about 9 minutes, which is typically about 5 to 10 messages at a time. The cost for such a system is about $25,000, which is about $625 per user.

Comparison with Telephone Answering Machines

Although voice mail vendors are aghast at the idea of comparing their systems with telephone answering machines, a comparison can be very revealing to any electronic mail planner. A typical answering machine is priced at $150 and is capable of storing 30 to 45 minutes' worth of calls. This type of answering machine, furthermore, has features such as remote call-in which allows its user to retrieve messages from a remote telephone. Although the answering machines do not allow messages to be broadcast and do not have CBMS-type features, they do compete quite favorably with using voice mail systems extensively as answering machines. In Rolm's cost justification, for example, it costs $70,000 to provide 125 users with a voice mail system, which is $560 per user. Although decreasing costs (the justification was done in 1984) have lowered this price to about $55,000, or $440 per user, a company could get the same relative impact for about one quarter the price if it purchased analog machines for its employees. This, however, is a very depersonalized way of lowering telephone answering costs.

Voice mail, of course, has numerous advantages over analog telephone answering machines, including the ability to network them together, the ability to broadcast messages, the ability to review and change messages, and greater security because of password protection; so, it is not necessarily a wise move to purchase telephone answering machines for each employee instead of a voice mail system. Nevertheless, the cost of answering machines provides a backdrop for a planner to evaluate the real value of a voice mail system; it also shows that advanced technology is not necessarily the most cost-effective means of getting the job done.

PCs and Voice Mail

Voice mail has moved from being based on minicomputers down to supermicros, and has recently migrated to PCs. A growing number of companies now offer voice processing boards that can turn a PC into a telephone answering machine, with roughly the same features as an analog machine. Such boards, however, are typically in the $600 to $900 range, which means that it is possible to create a digital solution for $3,000 that can be handled by an analog machine for $150. For obvious reasons, users are not flocking to such PC devices, although they do have a security advantage over an analog machine, whose messages can be retrieved by almost any remote call-in beeper device.

Integration with Text-Based CBMS

One of the long-term likelihoods in the industry is that voice and text technologies will merge. Already, Northern Telecom has demonstrated an integrated voice/text mail feature on its Meridian PBX. In an integrated system, users would be able to choose the most effective way to send a message so that someone who liked to type could use a keyboard, whereas those who preferred to speak their short messages could use the telephone. The receiver would then read the text messages on a screen and listen to the voice messages on the phone. Integrated systems, incidentally, presume that users have an all-digital network that can support such integration.

In an integrated system, it will also be possible to convert media so that text messages can be converted to spoken sounds. Numerous CBMS already have such an ability because of text-to-speech conversion devices. Going in the other direction — speech to text — is also possible, although it is presently very expensive. It will likely be the early 1990s before commercial-grade speech-to-text systems appear on the market.

Summary

Voice mail has been a relative disappointment in the market to date. The voice mail story shows how slowly new technologies can develop in a market where non-technical issues, such as user acceptance, the market channel, and competition for capital investment, are as important to a purchase decision as the technology itself. Readers should not get the idea, however, that voice mail has been a failure. The disappointment is based upon initial expectations, not upon any long-term potential for voice mail. As the cost of storage continues to plummet and the level of acceptance increases, it is almost a certainty that voice mail will obtain a relatively high penetration in the market and may one day be considered a necessity for any telephone system.

Corporate Mail Networks

The final, and most difficult, stage of any electronic mail implementation is developing a corporate electronic mail network. During this stage, the company must develop an electronic mail architecture that is capable of supporting all its employees, while also linking as many of the different electronic mail technologies together as possible. For large organizations, in particular, this stage usually requires a complete rethinking of previous electronic mail plans and system design.

Parameters of a Corporate Network

A corporate electronic mail network has parameters that differ markedly from a limited production system or even from multiple CBMS from the same software supplier that may be networked together. The reason is that a corporate mail network must:

- Interconnect all of the different CBMS operating in the company, not just CBMS from the same vendor;
- Develop an integrated directory for all the people on different mail systems on the network;
- Be capable of evolving into a backbone mail network that provides store-and-forward and sorting features for subscriber mail systems in the network;
- Anticipate interconnection with other electronic mail technologies, such as telex and facsimile;
- Provide gateways to public electronic mail services for intercompany communications and send next-day electronic business letters; and
- Handle other types of non-interactive business traffic, such as EDI and batch data processing files.

Although there are many CBMS that can send messages between compatible sister systems, unless the software is capable of handling all the above network-related parameters, it will most likely not meet the needs of a full, corporate electronic mail network, especially within larger organizations that have thousands of employees in many locations worldwide.

Basic Electronic Mail Access Methods

In general, CBMS hosts can be connected to users via a PBX, LAN, or traditional computer network. Figure 12-1 shows the three different types of CBMS roadways.

Figure 12-1. Basic Types of CBMS Access Methods

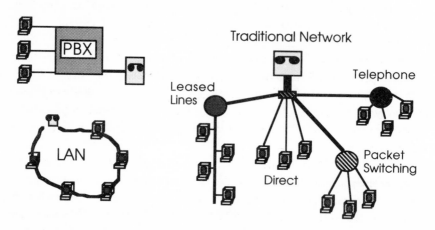

Although each type of network can operate with hosts of many sizes, in practice, most traditional-type CBMS are usually corporate mainframes or large minicomputers, PBX-based systems are usually supermicrocomputers or small minis, and LAN-based CBMS are supermicros or microcomputers. The most prevalent CBMS is based on a traditional architecture, with a large CBMS serving the needs of users from multiple locations within the organization. This type of CBMS typically has three different access methods, including hardwired, leased line, and public telephone network connections. These systems are also connecting to public or private packet networks with increasing frequency, which is a lower cost and more reliable alternative to the public telephone network.

LANs are the fastest growing network for CBMS. LAN-based CBMS usually operate for users within one LAN; thus, there may be several different CBMS servers on separate LANs within the building. Although many of these CBMS can only be accessed while users are on the LAN, the better LAN-based CBMS can also be accessed remotely via the telephone network or a packet switching network. Most LAN mail systems also can communicate with sister mail systems operating on other LANs so that they form a mail network for LAN users.

CBMS designed to operate on PBXs are set up for users within one building. These CBMS are the least common on the market, largely because the overwhelming majority of PBXs in operation do not yet have integrated voice/data operations. Typically, these CBMS can also be accessed remotely by direct telephone lines.

Basic CBMS Network Architectures

CBMS can be networked together as peers or via a backbone network. Networks themselves, furthermore, can be connected together via gateways, which are single entry points to a network that can accept messages to be routed to any node within the network. In a networking environment each CBMS has the ability to connect with every other CBMS in the network on a peer-to-peer basis. Few networks, however, have every node linked directly to every other node. Instead, CBMS are typically interlinked via leased lines to two other nodes. Messages are sent from the originating node and are passed from node to node through the network until they reach their destination nodes.

Network architecture is typically driven by the economics of leased lines. As the number of nodes increases, the number of lines required to support direct connections rises almost geometrically. For example, a network with 6 nodes requires 15 leased lines to interconnect each node to every other node, which is a 2.5:1 ratio of lines to nodes. A network with 30 nodes, however, requires 435 leased lines to interconnect every single point directly, which is a 14.5:1 ratio of lines to nodes. With the cost of computing power dropping in relationship to leased line costs, it is far more effective to put in more powerful computers and to pass messages through multiple nodes than it is to support the costs of multiple leased lines so that every node can exchange messages directly.

A backbone-mail network makes a distinction between switching nodes and subscriber nodes. The subscriber nodes handle mailbox and user interface tasks, whereas the switching nodes pass messages along to other switching nodes. The backbone nodes form a ring of switching stations that operate atop the subscriber nodes, which connect to backbone nodes in a star configuration as shown in Figure 12-2. Subscriber nodes pass their messages up to a backbone node, which sorts the messages and either passes them down to other subscriber nodes that are supported locally or over to another backbone node that performs the same task.

There are four parameters that determine whether a company should use a backbone CBMS switching architecture or whether it should allow its subscriber CBMS to operate in a peer-to-peer network:

• The volume of intersystem traffic between nodes;

- The number of incompatible systems in the network;
- The physical location of the various subscriber nodes; and
- Other applications that might share the backbone node.

Figure 12-2. Backbone Network Architecture

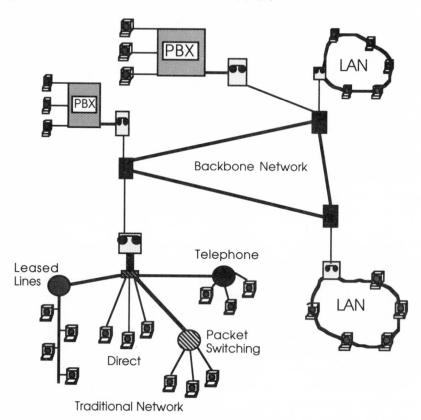

The first parameter is traffic load on the network. As the number of CBMS increases, it becomes less costly, more efficient, and more reliable to use a backbone network configured for sorting and routing messages amongst subscriber nodes than to have every node share the sorting and routing load. The reason is that a computer network generates an inevitable number of administrative messages related to tasks such as changes in network directories, network software changes, and error messages when a message cannot be delivered. As the number of nodes increases, administrative messages often multiply at a much faster rate, resulting in decreased network performance. Although a network with a backbone architecture requires computers that are dedicated solely to message switching tasks, it can often operate with greater efficiency and lower overall cost than a peer-to-peer network.

The second parameter is the number of different CBMS operating on the network. If there are four or five different types of CBMS on the network, it is often more cost-effective for each one to run message transport software compatible to the backbone network's protocol than for each different system to operate on separate internal networks with gateways that provide entry points across the different networks. For example, if there are four different mail systems (A, B, C, and D) that must be interconnected, six gateways must be written so that each network can intercommunicate (A-B, A-C, A-D, B-C, B-D, and C-D). In contrast, for all four types of systems to communicate in a backbone network (E), only four different message transport versions must be written (A, B, C, and D).

The third parameter is the location of the systems. If the systems are equally distributed throughout the network so that each facility has multiple mail systems from different vendors, then it likely will be more efficient for the different systems to all communicate to one backbone at the facility than to operate as three separate leased line networks. If, on the other hand, the systems are typically located at different facilities, it may be more effective to operate each system on a separate network with gateways between the networks.

The fourth parameter is traffic from other applications that can share the backbone network. Although a corporate mail network may not generate enough traffic by itself to justify a backbone network, additional non-interactive applications that share the network, such as batch data transfer, electronic documents, formatted computer programs, EDI, and internal business forms, may justify its installation.

The technical details of network architectures is a complex subject that is beyond the scope of this book. Most users, furthermore, are faced with more direct problems, such as interlinking their existing three or four different private mail systems with a public service to support 2,000 to 3,000 users, which represents 5 to 10 percent of their white collar employees. These companies, at present, are more interested in short-term solutions to connect existing systems, than in any long-term architectures that will require a backbone network to connect 50,000 people operating on 150 nodes. Planners, however, should not make the mistake of sacrificing long-term for short-term gains. The sooner a long-term architecture is chosen, the less likely the company will be to run into problems such as having a network that cannot meet user demand.

Case Study of Digital Equipment's Internal Mail System

Digital Equipment Corp.'s internal mail network shows how a backbone network for electronic mail naturally evolves from a trial to a production system to a corporate network. Digital's first electronic mail system was born in 1974 as a traditional message switching system in which messages were auto-delivered to 81 terminals located in communication centers throughout the company. By 1979, the message network had grown to 500 terminals worldwide.

The Trial Stage

In 1978, the company authorized its first CBMS trial, using the Comet mail system from CCA in Cambridge, Mass. Within a year, the CBMS pilot grew from 40 initial users to 650 users with mailbox addresses. These users estimated productivity improvements of from 5 to 15 percent, which was enough to convince the company to move to a limited production system even though hard dollar savings could not be proven. According to a paper entitled "The Evolution of a Corporate Electronic Mail Network", written by David Whitten of Digital in May 1985 for the International Communications Association's 38th Annual Conference and Exposition:

> The production proposal was accepted despite the fact that financial analysis conducted at the conclusion of the pilot did not show sufficient hard dollar savings for a level of return on investment to justify its implementation. The major contributing factor to the proposal's acceptance by Digital's senior management committee was their own experience as users during the pilot. These individuals were able to personally corroborate the soft, productivity improvement savings of electronic mail usage generally cited by the pilot group.

Limited Production System

Upon completion of the pilot, Digital decided to switch to a production system developed in-house because of the requirement to have multiple nodes in the network. It also decided to use the company's existing corporate message switching system to transfer messages between the different nodes. In 1980, the production system went into operation and grew within 2 years from 650 users in the trial system to 8,600 users operating on 13 separate nodes.

During the same period, Digital's engineers were using their own electronic mail system built as a utility to Digital's RSTS and VMS operating systems. About 20,000 engineers used the internal mail utility as part of an informal network. Unlike the corporate mail system, there were no formal operating procedures; thus, reliability was not guaranteed. The system, however, satisfied the needs of its users to the point that they had no desire to switch to the corporate system.

Because interconnection was necessary between the two networks, a gateway was built in 1981, which introduced two new factors to the network. First, because the engineering system had no formal reliability parameters, message transfer could not be guaranteed. Second, there was no way to estimate the impact on traffic that would result from the interconnection of the networks. The interconnection resulted in a rapid growth of traffic, with frequent delays and message backlogs because of the gateway.

During this same period, the number of different mail systems within Digital also started to multiply. Digital, for example, developed a new mail package as part of its ALL-IN-1 integrated office software. As a result, Digital was faced with adding these new mail systems to its rapidly expanding network.

Evolution of a Corporate Network

Digital learned the hard way that mail traffic can grow beyond the ability of a limited production system to handle worldwide demands. According to the paper written by David Whitten:

> The situation we faced was a complex one—internal organizations with varying requirements, using partial solutions, all had legitimate business reasons for wanting the capability to exchange messages with one another.
>
> It seemed that the list of available mail systems was continually expanding. While each organization had good reasons for preferring the system it had implemented, no single system appeared to meet the overall set of requirements.
>
> It was obvious that a completely homogeneous mail network would not—could not—solve our problem.

Digital solved its problem by developing an architecture based on the standards work done by the International Federation of Information Processors (IFIP) and the National Bureau of Standards (NBS). In the architecture the message transmission portion of the system (message transfer agent) is separated from the user portion of the system (user agent) so that back end system-to-system message transport can take place without the users on any specific system changing the way in which they operate. According to the paper by David Whitten:

> The concept of formally separating message transport services from user agent services is a powerful one. Using the concept, we realized that we could build a single "message bus" that would carry store-and-forward messages throughout the corporation. The transport service could use a single well-defined message format and well-specified application protocols. However, we could still allow each organization to choose a mail system according to its individual requirements for a subscriber interface. A mail system, to be eligible for interconnection, would simply have to meet the standards of message format and protocol imposed by the message-transport service.

Digital implemented its message transport service through software that became the company's Message Router product. Initially, it implemented Message Router via a gateway to prove that it would work. Its second step was to develop a pilot network in which Message Router served as a backbone for several of Digital's mail systems. The pilot network went into operation in the spring of 1983 and became Digital's official mail architecture in the fall of 1983. Since then, Digital's mail network has grown from 8,600 to close to 65,000 users.

The Network Directory Issue

When Digital operated its early corporate mail system, it used an online directory of all users that was duplicated on all 13 nodes in the network. When a user typed in an ID or an address list, the names were verified in real-time, and the routing information was added to each address automatically— so that the user knew immediately whether the address was accurate— and the system worried about routing details. Although such a directory is powerful, it also had some serious problems related to handling growth. According to Whitten's paper:

> The universal directory maintenance process had resulted in generating an unmanageable level of overhead traffic and this design could not be supported in a larger network. We had measured this traffic and found that anywhere from 30 percent to 60 percent of the messages delivered

between nodes were directory related overhead messages! A quick calculation showed that a network the size
of our proposed MTS (Message Transport Service), having
hundreds of nodes and tens of thousands of subscribers,
would consume all but a few percent of its capacity with
directory update messages.

As a result, Digital had to sacrifice an online, real-time directory in order
to develop a corporate mail network capable of supporting all its employees.
Figure 12-3 shows a diagram of how Digital's corporate message network
operates.

Figure 12-3. Operation of Digital's Corporate Message System

Sorting Node Directory		
Mail system subscribers at supported facilities	Non-mail subscribers at supported facilities	
Sorting Node Transfer System		
Reception of traffic from subscriber systems	Sorting of mail for other nodes in backbone network	Delivery of mail to mail systems and mailroom printers

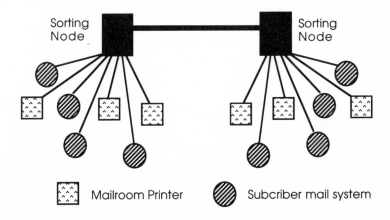

Mailroom Printer   Subcriber mail system

In Digital's present network every node keeps a directory of the company's mail routing codes, along with the directory of its local users. Digital's backbone sorting nodes also house copies of every subscriber node directory that it supports so that the sorting node can decide whether an address is correct. This prevents incorrectly addressed messages from flowing throughout the entire system. Such a message is captured before it leaves the backbone network. Although it means that user names are duplicated once in the system, the overhead has proven acceptable.

Digital also made an important choice in how users address messages. Rather than creating a new set of addressing codes, such as the name of the mail system, Digital uses its well known internal mail system routing codes so that new users are immediately familiar with the addressing scheme. The directories then map the internal routing code to the address of the appropriate delivery vehicle. Digital's network has a significant feature which sets it apart from many other mail systems. The directory houses all employees in the company, not just mailbox users. When a message is addressed to a user without a mailbox, it is routed to a printer in the closest corporate mailroom and then delivered via the regular internal mail system. This gives Digital a truly companywide system.

Messages are routed through the network from a subscriber node to a sorting node, which is connected via a backbone network to other sorting nodes. Messages flow up to a sorting node, through the backbone network, and down to the appropriate subscriber node or mailroom printer.

Lessons Learned

The evolution of Digital's internal mail network illustrates a number of the principles of planning and implementation. First, Digital assured success for the project by getting top management involved from the very beginning. The project may well have been killed if a number of top managers were not part of the initial trial. Second, Digital integrated non-direct users into the system so that it has a true message delivery network, not just a mailbox CBMS. It even duplicated its well known mail routing codes as part of the mail network's addressing structure. Third, Digital had well defined implementation phases that led from a trial to a limited production system to a full network.

Lessons from Other Large Networks

Digital, of course, is not the only company that has implemented a sizeable mail network. For example, there is one large Fortune 100 company, which has asked not to be identified, that has a network that supports more than 20,000 users worldwide. Unlike Digital's network, this company's system is completely centralized on IBM mainframes at corporate headquarters. There is no backbone network. Every user, except those at corporate headquarters, communicates through a long distance network to reach the mail system.

Although the company incurs naturally higher communication costs than does Digital, which only incurs telecommunication costs when messages are transferred via the backbone network, the firm has maintained central control of its directory, enabling it to provide a unique feature. Every user has a profile that not only includes the basics, such as name and address, but also includes the type of word processor that he or she uses. When a user creates a message, it can be done on any one of several word processors supported by the company, such as Multimate, Wang, or IBM Displaywrite. The system will then automatically translate the format of the message from the sender's word processor to the receiver's word processor.

The company's network also has an integrated computer conferencing system; thus, users can choose to send messages or attend electronic meetings. According to usage statistics, users spend almost as much time in conferences as they do in sending messages. The company, in short, has focused its efforts on two other major planning principles. First, it has avoided line editors at all costs. Second, it has looked at all the different electronic mail technologies and integrated computer conferencing into its basic network.

Choosing a Corporate Mail Architecture

Digital's and the other company's mail networks are complete contrasts in style: One is highly decentralized and the other is highly centralized. Both, however, meet the needs of their organizations. The key lesson that cuts across both companies is that they carefully chose their architectures with a full understanding of their limitations. Digital sacrificed directory control in order to gain independence for its diverse user groups to choose their own user agents. Although this requires each user agent to conform to a message transfer agent format, it does provide freedom of choice for users in the company. The other company is locked into one mail system for everyone in the company. Interestingly, however, this has allowed users to have freedom in defining the editor that they use to interact with the system and has also allowed integration of another electronic mail technology: computer conferencing.

Which architecture is better? The answer, of course, is neither one. The architecture fits the style of each company. Digital, for example, could never have chosen a homogeneous system because of its strong-willed user groups that each wanted its own mail system. The other company, in contrast, has a user population that has been willing to take the lead from its central technology planning group. A big plus has been providing freedom to users in an area they do care about— choosing individual word processors.

The first and only rule of choosing a corporate mail architecture is that it must reflect the company's technology style. Organizations with a highly centralized control of technology may find a centralized mail network appropriate, especially if it enables them to have a high degree of directory control and to implement special features. Organizations with a great degree of autonomy, on the other hand, may already have several different mail systems or networks in operation, along with a bottom-up demand for LANs and LAN-based mailbox systems. This type of organization will be better served by initially interlinking its systems via gateways and then evolving to a consistent architecture based on a single backbone network.

Cost is also a factor. In a centralized mail network, every session will incur a communication cost, except those held at the location where the mail system is located. In a decentralized network, only messages that require remote transfer will incur a communications cost. Thus, it is almost a certainty that a decentralized mail architecture, especially one based on a backbone network, will incur lower communication costs. Still, there are other tradeoffs here. A centralized mail architecture places operational control in the hands of one group, which allows a high degree of reliability in system operation, although it presents a greater target for system security. A networked system has a much higher chance of variations in the way each node is operated, although its decentralized nature gives it greater overall security. The operational problem can be particularly acute in a company with dozens of different mail systems on LANs. Each system must develop its own procedures for backing up files and maintaining system integrity. In practice, each organization must decide whether to trade off lower communication costs and the higher security of a decentralized network for the higher operational reliability of a centralized network.

X.400 as a Mail Architecture

When planners opt for a backbone or peer-to-peer electronic mail network based on separating the message transfer agent from the user agent portion of subscriber mail systems, they must adopt the appropriate message transport protocol to be used throughout the network. Each mail system must adhere to this protocol or build a gateway to participate in the network. Choosing the correct protocol is obviously critical because it will impact on network operations for years.

I have an open bias for this choice: X.400, the international message transfer Standard developed by CCITT and supported by the International Standards Organization (ISO) as the Message-Oriented Text Information

System (MOTIS) Standard. X.400 has one purpose: *Its adoption will lead to the development of a worldwide network to exchange electronic mail messages and other types of data.*

Choosing X.400 has implications beyond the narrow interests of an organization's message system. X.400 is a good social choice as well as a technological choice. X.400, of course, will not save the world. It is, however, one small cog in the development of a worldwide communications infrastructure that will make it easier for people to intercommunicate on a global basis. If all else is equal, this is the social factor that should sway organizations to choose X.400.

Implementation of X.400

X.400 has already won the support of most telecommunications authorities and major computer companies around the world. IBM, in fact, is the only major computer company that has not already committed to supporting X.400 as the native protocol for its non-interactive message, data, and file transfer network, which means that a serious choice of a long-term backbone mail architecture is really between IBM's proprietary architecture, SNADS (SNA Delivery Systems), and X.400. Although IBM will not support X.400 directly, it has committed to providing X.400 gateways to its electronic mail products in Canada and Europe by late 1988. While IBM does not plan to release the X.400 gateways in the U.S., it has made a public statement that its direction on X.400 will be driven by customer demand.

X.400 is now out of the development labs and implemented in a number of commercial systems and public services. At the Hanover Fair in Germany in March 1987, 14 vendors came together in an international demonstration of X.400 products. The companies are British Telecom, Groupe Bull, Data General, Digital Equipment Corp., Deutsche Bundespost, Hewlett-Packard, International Computers Ltd., Nippon Telephone & Telegraph, Nixdorf, Olivetti, NV Philips, Siemens Data Systems, Sydney Development Corp., and Xerox.

Sydney Development Corp. (Vancouver, B.C.) is the smallest firm on the list, yet it is one of the most significant because it is licensing operational X.400 software to companies worldwide for usage in their own products. Sydney's customers include AES Ltd. and Northern Telecom (Canada); Data General and AT&T (U.S.A.); Olivetti, Nixdorf, and Siemens (Germany); Hasler, Xmit, and Radio Swisse (Switzerland); Info Technology (U.K.); and Standard Telephone (Norway). Sydney is important because it points the way to how X.400 software is likely to be implemented in the market. Instead of companies developing their own versions, most will opt to purchase X.400 modules on an OEM (Original Equipment Manufacturer) basis for inclusion into their electronic mail products. Competitors to Sydney are already in the market and are driving the price down for X.400 software modules.

In October 1987 at Telecom '87 in Geneva, private system vendors and public mail services gave a second demonstration of X.400 transfer capabilities amongst 21 different systems and services. In addition, the Corporation for Open Systems (COS) in the United States took another important step towards the implementation of X.400 by announcing a formal conformance testing procedure to assure that software for the U.S. market meets X.400 specifications. COS's X.400 efforts are part of a worldwide conformance testing network for X.400, with counterparts operating in Europe. Conformance testing is a critical element in the implementation of any Standard, especially a complex one such as X.400 that must meet compatibility tests at seven levels. (See Chapter 4 for a brief description of X.400's seven layers of operation.) Conformance testing is a sign that X.400 is ready for widespread commercial implementation.

X.400 Message Transfer Protocols

X.400 is the overall CCITT Standard that governs the exchange of messages amongst various message handling systems. Its counterpart Standard in ISO is MOTIS, which is almost identical to X.400. The major difference is that while the CCITT's X.400 Standard is designed to foster development of a public worldwide electronic mail network administered by telecommunication agencies, the MOTIS Standard is set up so that private X.400 systems can communicate directly via a variety of ISO-standardized communication networks, including leased lines, packet networks and Local Area Networks. In the CCITT's structure, public X.400 services are called Administrative Domains (ADMs), while private systems connecting into the public network are called Private Domains (PRDMs).

X.400's basic power comes from a separation of User Agents (UAs), which handle the interface to users, and Message Transfer Agents (MTAs), which transfer messages to UAs and between other MTAs. UAs may reside on the same host as the MTA, or one UA may be in a separate physical entity, such as a PC. There are three basic protocols associated with X.400: P1, P2, and P3, which are shown in Figure 12-4. P1 is the Message Transfer Protocol that determines how two MTAs exchange messages. P3 is the protocol that determines how a remote UA on a personal computer exchanges messages with an MTA. P2 is the protocol that is used to transfer interpersonal messaging application information between two UAs. This information is encapsulated by the P1 and P3 protocols so that it is transferred transparently by the message transport service. Readers will also notice in Figure 12-4 that there is a Submission and Delivery Entity, which handles the transfer of information between an MTA and a UA.

The P1, P2, and P3 protocols all operate at different sub-levels of the application layer of the OSI reference model, which is important. The Message Transfer Layer (MTL) is where the P1 and P3 protocols operate, which allows messages to be transferred between two systems transparently from the User Agent Layer (UAL), which is where the cooperating UAs perform their processing functions on the information passed by the MTAs.

Figure 12-4. X.400 Message Transfer Protocols

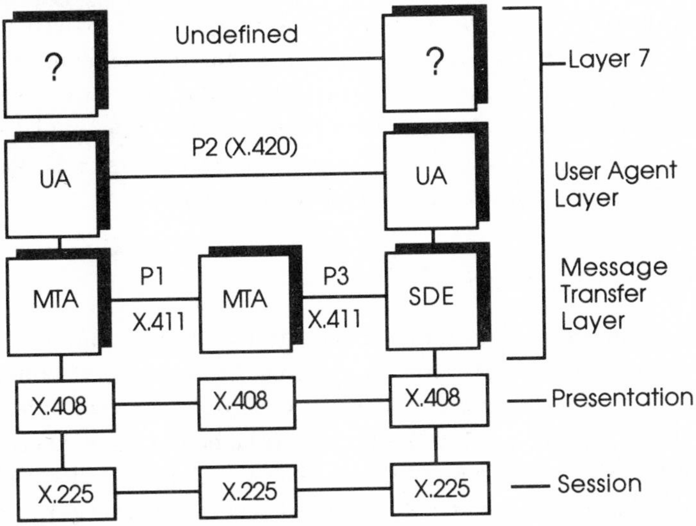

Technological Strength of X.400

X.400 is a highly complex Standard that is capable of meeting the full needs of a company's non-interactive message traffic. Figure 12-5 shows the basic design of X.400's MHS (Message Handling Service), which consists of service elements for both the MTA and UA, along with the content of the message. The service elements are fields that contain descriptions about the message or instructions on how the message should be handled. Included in Figure 12-5 are the service elements for the MTA. UA service elements are described later in the chapter. X.400's flexibility in handling messages comes from separating the MTA service elements from the header and contents of the message. The MTA service elements handle exchanging messages with other MTAs and with UAs, while UAs handle encoding and decoding the header, which contains the UA service elements, and assembling or delivering the contents in the body of the message to the user.

The MTA is divided into five separate areas: Basic, Submission and Delivery, Conversion, Query, and Status and Information. Each of these areas consists of specific service elements that determine the features that are available when passing messages. The Basic service elements must be supported by all MTAs. The other service elements are optional, which means that an MTA does not have to support the requests made by other MTAs, such as providing multiple grades of delivery, although an MTA must recognize that such a request has been made, so that a notification can be returned that the requested service was not performed.

Figure 12-5. Basic Design of X.400 Message Transport Service

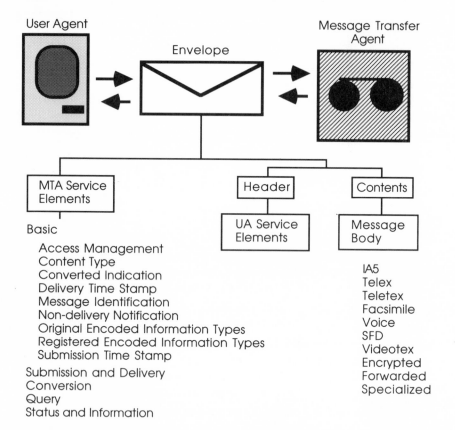

From the basic service elements, the role of the MTA becomes clear. The MTA performs these basic functions:

- Validates that it is talking with a registered MTA;
- Validates that the recipient is registered on the system;
- Identifies the Content Type to determine which type of information is being delivered;
- Indicates whether the message being received has been converted from a different information type;

- Identifies the time that a message was received from another MTA;
- Identifies the time a message was sent to another MTA;
- Places a unique identifier on each message transmitted, consisting of the system where the message originated and the unique number;
- Sends a notification to the sending MTA if the message cannot be delivered properly for a variety of reasons, including an improper address or encoded information type that cannot be received; and
- Looks at the type of information in the message and converts it to the type of information that the recipient can receive.

The MTA also has a sophisticated submission and delivery system that includes numerous options specifying the grade of delivery service, delivery notification and time options, and multidestination delivery requirements. X.400 also allows the MTA to make probes about whether messages and their specific contents can be delivered to specific UAs, which allows users to determine whether a message can be transmitted successfully.

Two of the MTA's most important capabilities are tracking the content types and the original encoded information types. The content type within X.400 refers to the specific application for the message, not the types of encoded information included in the message. At present, the CCITT has identified two content types: an Interpersonal Message and an Interpersonal Message status report, which contains information such as a receipt from a UA that a message has been delivered to its user.

The original encoded information type identifies the specific format of the information being transmitted. On an international level, the original encoded information types field identifies nine basic types of message formats, including International Alphabet #5, telex, teletex, Groups 3 and 4 facsimile, voice, videotex, mixed mode (teletex and facsimile), and what the CCITT terms a simple formattable document (SFD), which is a series of paragraphs that can be formatted for the user by the UA. In addition, X.400 also defines information types for encrypted information, forwarded information and nationally-defined information, which can be used to define a non-standard information type.

The original encoded information types service element is used with the registered encoded information types and converted indication service elements to provide automatic format translation between different information types. This works by users registering the types of information they can receive. In theory, when the MTA receives a message, it checks the recipient's registered original encoded information types service element and performs any required file conversions. In practice, vendors are not yet implementing this capability, the main purpose of which is to allow messages sent from terminals and PCs to be converted for delivery to telex, teletex, and facsimile networks, which are designated as telematic services by the CCITT. While X.400 networks will operate with telematic services, it is not yet clear whether the providers will implement these connections using X.400's structure or a proprietary structure that achieves the same result.

In addition, it also is not clear whether suppliers will expand X.400's format conversion capabilities to include a wide variety of non-standard document formats, such as word processing program formats and spreadsheets, or whether such format conversion services will be provided independently of X.400's structure. It is clear, however, that suppliers believe that format translation services are important for electronic mail networks and will be providing these capabilities as part of an overall message handling service.

User Agent

The User Agent represents users on an X.400 mail system. Two UAs communicate together by service elements, which allow common mail system functions to be performed across X.400 systems, such as indicating the subject; replying to, forwarding, and auto-forwarding messages; and requesting a return receipt. Advanced service elements can also be performed, such as sending multiple information types within one message (multi-part body), encrypting messages, and sending cross-references to other messages.

The best way to understand the UA service elements is by thinking of general functions that must be performed. Each general function has a series of service elements associated with it, each of which performs a task required to complete the overall function. These functions provide information about the:

- Sender and recipients;
- Relationship that the message has to other messages;
- Contents and handling of the message; and
- Delivery status of the message.

The UA service elements are listed in Figure 12-6 under the general function that they perform.

The service elements that provide information about the sender and recipients are **originator, authorizing users, primary recipients, copy recipients** and **blind copy recipients.** The **originator** service element identifies the sender of the message. The **authorizing users** service element identifies users who are authorized to access the recipient's mailbox. The **primary recipients** are the users who are identified in the **To:** field of the message. The **copy recipients** are those who receive copies of the message. The **blind copy** recipients are those who receive copies, but are not identified in any list of copy recipients.

The service elements that describe the various relationships the message has to other messages on the system are the **message ID, reply to** indication, **forwarded** indication, **obsoleting** indication and **cross reference** indication. The **message ID** provides a unique ID for the message. The **reply to** indication identifies that the message is in reply to a specific message sent by the recipient previously. The **forwarded** indication tells that the message was received previously by the sender and is being forwarded to the recipient. The **obsoleting** indicator tells that the message is obsoleting a specific message received by the recipient. The **cross reference** indicator tells that the message is related to a specific message already received by the recipient.

Figure 12-6. Optional Cooperating UA Service Elements

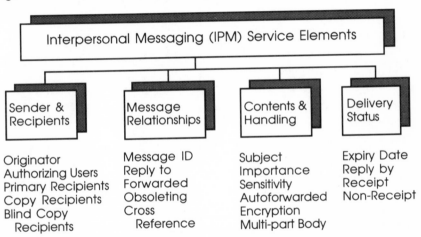

The service elements that describe information about the contents and handling of the message are **subject, importance, sensitivity, autoforwarded, body part encryption** and **multi-part body**. The **subject** indicates the subject of the message as described by the sender. The **importance** indicates whether the sender has assigned a low, normal or high importance to the message. The **sensitivity** indicates whether the sender considers the message personal, private or open to anyone (computer conference). **Autoforwarded** indicates that the sender is automatically forwarding the message to a specific recipient. Autoforwarding is used when people are away from the mailboxes and have authorized other people to receive their messages. The **body part encryption** indicator tells that the message's body is encrypted. The **multi-part body** indication tells that the body of the message has multiple encoded information types, such as a document with integrated text and facsimile.

The service elements that describe delivery status are the **expiry date** indication, **reply by** indication, **non-receipt notification** and **receipt notification**. The **expiry date** indication tells when the sender wants the message to be destroyed if it has not been read by the recipient. The **reply by** indication tells the recipient the date when the sender wishes to have a reply. The **non-receipt notification** tells the recipient's UA that the sender wishes to be notified if the receiver decides not to read the message, while the **receipt notification** tells the recipient's UA that the sender wishes to be told when the message is read.

X.400 Message Domains and Directories

The CCITT has designated two types of X.400 systems — Administrative Domains (ADMs) and Private Domains (PRDMs). An Administrative Domain is a public mail service operated by an authorized telecommunications organization. In most countries, this will be the Postal, Telephone & Telegraph (PTT) authority. A Private Domain is operated by a private organization, such as a commercial company or government organization. In the CCITT's view of X.400, Private Domain networks will use public Administrative Domains to handle most of their inter-company message traffic. In this way, a worldwide network of X.400 Administrative and Private Domains is expected to evolve. The ISO's MOTIS Standard, however, allows private X.400 systems to communicate directly independent of the CCITT's Administrative Domain structure. This opens up a wide variety of options for users to configure and operate X.400 message systems.

At present, X.400 has no directory structure, although it has a standardized addressing structure. Users know how addresses, called O/R (Originator/Recipient) names, must be designated in an X.400 system, but they have no way of searching a directory to find out a user's proper name unless the directory is provided in a proprietary fashion by the X.400 supplier. A standardized directory structure, however, is critical for the development of a worldwide X.400 network. The CCITT's Study Group VII, which develops the X.400 Standards, has already developed the specifications for a worldwide directory structure to be adopted in 1988. The new Directory Standard, which is called X.500, is one of the keys to the development of national and worldwide electronic mail networks for inter-company communications.

The X.500 Directory Standard operates in a similar fashion to an X.400 mail system, but is an independent entity. Every system with an MTA will have a directory that will support local UAs and will also recognize how to send search requests to the directories associated with other MTAs. By knowing the name of the recipient, the Private Domain, and the Administrative Domain that services the Private Domain, it will be possible for a sender to have a message routed worldwide for delivery. If the sender does not know the correct name of the Domain, but knows the recipient's name, it will also be possible to search directories worldwide to find the recipient.

Figure 12-7 shows how the domain and directory structures will operate. An Administrative Domain, as a public service, will keep a directory that houses the names of its local users, of the Private Domains that it services, and of all public Administrative Domains in the world (or at least the ones with which it has formal interconnections). When a message is sent for delivery, it must have the names of the Administrative Domain, Private Domain, and recipient, so that the message can be routed and delivered.

Figure 12-7. Domain Structure of X.400 Networks

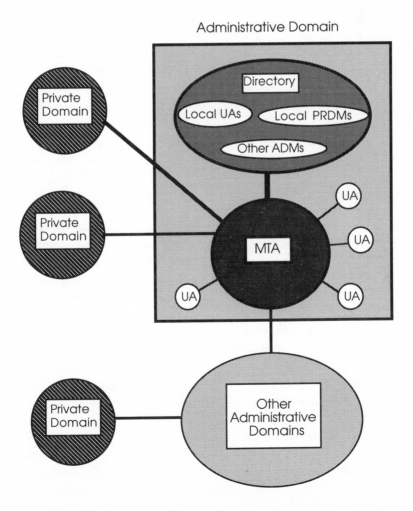

Without all three names, the sender must perform a directory search to find the missing information. Let's say that a sender in France wishes to send a message to John Jones in ABC Company in the U.S., but does not know the specific Administrative Domain that services ABC Company. The sender would submit a directory search request to the Adminstrative Domain in France, which would send it to any Administrative Domain in the U.S. If that Domain served ABC Company, it would send back that it could handle the delivery. If not, the U.S. Domain would forward the search request to another U.S. Domain and to another until a match were found. In practice, since a search request could be forwarded forever if a match were not found, each request will have a limit on the number of times it can be forwarded to another directory. When the limit is reached, the request will be returned to the initiator with a message that its parameters cannot be matched.

Users will also be able to use the directory system to make probes of whether a message can be delivered. This will prevent a user from sending a lengthy message, for which the sender will be charged, only to discover that the recipient's name or Private Domain was not properly listed. A probe is a request from an MTA asking whether a specific type of encoded information can be delivered to a specific recipient. The MTA sends the probe as if it were sending a message and receives a notification from the recipient's MTA whether it can properly deliver the type of information requested. When a probe is returned with a positive response, the sender can then ship the full message with assurance that it can be delivered.

Connection to Voice Mail and Telematic Services

X.400 is designed to allow integration with voice mail and Telematic services such as facsimile, telex, and teletex. In the United States, where most CBMS are already integrated with telex, the immediate advantage will come from integration with facsimile machines, which are now spreading rapidly within most companies. This will allow a company to get additional usage from facsimile machines by allowing the mail system to direct messages to each facsimile machine in the organization. To give an example of where the connection will be valuable, it will allow the X.400 system to send messages to non-direct users via the growing base of facsimile machines in an organization. It will also allow desktop publishing systems to deliver their output to a wide network of printing devices that can handle integrated text and graphics documents. As X.400 evolves it will also allow voice mail systems to be integrated with text mail systems. Initially, most UAs will not be capable of handling voice messages even if they can receive them. As technology continues to develop, however, voice mail integration will become natural.

X.400 Applications

At this writing, X.400 performs one application — exchanging Interpersonal Messages. Its architecture, however, allows X.400 to be enhanced so that it can support the delivery of information from multiple applications. Already, for example, there are standards groups in several countries, including the National Bureau of Standards (NBS) in the U.S., that are working on the issue of standardizing an application for machine to machine information exchanges, such as Electronic Data Interchange (EDI), using X.400's architecture.

The ability to develop multiple applications is critical to X.400's future because it not only opens the door to several national and international standardized applications, but also will allow users to develop their own applications for use on their internal networks. Readers should keep in mind, however, that it will take several years before today's X.400 products evolve to the point where they can be used to develop additional applications with ease. Not only will suppliers have to implement X.400 directly into their electronic mail products, but also they will have to provide the software tools to develop the specific applications.

Types Of Applications

X.400 is suitable for non-interactive applications in which the information does not have to be exchanged between sender and receiver in real-time. Interpersonal Messaging is a perfect example. Other potential applications include:

- Electronic Data Interchange (EDI) — the exchange of business trade documents like purchase orders, invoices and shipping manifests;
- Electronic Funds Transfer;
- Internal data processing transmissions, such as orders, personnel payroll data, inventory data and internal business forms;
- Document distribution;
- Financial planning, including the transmission of spreadsheets, graphics, and data base information; and
- Exchange of engineering-related information, such as CAD/CAM files.

Support For Multiple Applications

The key to supporting multiple applications within X.400 comes from:
- Allowing the MTA to recognize both content types (applications) and original encoded information types (file format of the message's body type);

- Placing the MTA below the UA at OSI's 7th layer; and
- Having a single directory that can be used for multiple applications.

To see how X.400 can be used for non-standard applications, the National Bureau of Standards in the U.S. has already defined an interim solution that allows EDI documents to be transmitted using an X.400 system, even though EDI is not yet a part of the X.400 Standard. Companies who wish to exchange EDI documents using this solution must recognize the proprietary content type and the special addresses. The NBS interim solution, incidentally, was developed under a request from the Canadian Manufacturer's Association, which plans to use X.400 as a means of interconnecting various EDI services so that users on the different services can exchange EDI documents.

The NBS interim solution for EDI is the prelude to a new protocol that is now being planned for X.400. The protocol will allow machine to machine information transfer, in addition to the person to person transfer in the present version. At this writing, the NBS in the U.S. and several other groups in other countries are starting the process of defining the service elements for the new protocol. It will be several years, however, before the protocol is defined and adopted as an official Standard.

X.400's 1988 Version

The X.400 systems that are now on the market adhere to the 1984 specifications adopted by the CCITT. In 1988, the CCITT will issue a new set of specifications for X.400 that have several important enhancements, including improved encryption capabilities, interworking with the X.500 Directory Standard, postal internetworking among Administrative Domains, and a Message Store that is designed to allow users on PCs and other remote workstations to have their messages stored in a central system, but to read and create messages while offline on the workstations. The Message Store will be used as part of a redefined P3 protocol.

While these enhancements are important for X.400's evolution, they add an unsettling element to the industry because vendors have worked almost three years to introduce commercial X.400 products and services that conform to the 1984 specifications. Because many of these companies will wish to receive some return on their already substantial investment, it will likely be several years before existing X.400 products are upgraded to meet the 1988 version of the Standard. Not only will the vendors have to make considerable enhancements to add the Message Store and support interaction with an X.500 Directory, in addition, they will have to implement the Directory itself, which is a major development.

In short, while today's commercial X.400 products and services are a major step in the evolution of a worldwide messaging system, they are really just the first of many steps that must be taken over the next decade before X.400's impact is felt by users on a global scale. While this can be frustrating for users who want immediate needs met as soon as possible, we should all keep in mind that the electronic messaging industry has achieved as much in one decade as the telephone industry achieved in its first century. The first commercial telephone systems were introduced in the 1870s, with voice grade underseas cables installed in the 1950s to allow worldwide telephone communications. The first electronic mail services went public in the late 1970s and already the rudiments of a worldwide network are available commercially.

Evolving a Corporate Network Gracefully

Although companies must choose a mail architecture, the choice does not mean immediate, radical changes to the company's existing mail network. Instead, whatever architecture is chosen can be implemented gracefully over a period of a few years. Most large companies today, for example, have several private mail systems operating on mainframes or minis, a growing number of small mail systems operating on LANs or PBXs, and a few departments operating on public services.

The first step for most of these companies will have little to do with choosing any long-term architecture. Initially, most companies will want to connect their existing mail systems together, probably via gateways. As overall demand for mail services becomes clearer, companies will adopt a long-term architecture for interconnecting mail systems, with the most likely choice being some combination of X.400 and SNADS. Once this architecture is chosen, a trial should be set up involving a few nodes to make certain that it works. When the architecture is proven, implementation can evolve rapidly, with nodes joining the network in controlled fashion. One positive factor is the power that a network holds for all users within an organization. As soon as the network is publicized, many people on the different systems in operation will ask to join it.

Interim Gateway Strategy

Although evolving a full electronic mail network architecture will likely take a few years or more, particularly because of the network administration issue, interim interconnection needs can be met very quickly via software gateways. These gateways translate the envelope structure of one mail system into the envelope structure of another system, allowing messages to be passed between the systems, although there is a price that must be paid. Because each message must have its envelope translated, gateways have considerable processing overhead; thus, performance slows down as volumes increase. When a number of large networks are interconnected via gateways, volume often increases far more rapidly than the gateway can handle, causing a traffic bottleneck. Users, furthermore, quickly become dependent upon the gateway to enable communications across networks, resulting in considerable user dissatisfaction.

The gateway strategy also runs into a serious problem as the number of different systems that must be interconnected grows. Although 3 systems require 3 separate gateways, 5 different systems require 10 gateways, and 10 different systems require 45 gateways. For this reason, gateways quickly lose their appeal as the number of incompatible systems increases. Nevertheless, when a company must interconnect 2 or 3 different networks, using a gateway is the fastest means available in the market today.

Soft-Switch's DAD Gateway

There is one company, Soft-Switch (King of Prussia, Penn.), that has developed a gateway product that can interlink more than 8 different mail systems without requiring 28 different gateways, as would normally be the case. The product is called DAD, which is an acronym for DIU Assembler/Disassembler. The DIU (Document Interchange Unit) is based on IBM's DIA and extends DIA to other vendors' mail and document formats. The DAD, according to Soft-Switch, intercepts intersystem mail from the originating system, translates it to a universal envelope format, and sends it to a DAD at the recipient system, which retranslates the envelope to the recipient system's format. At this writing, Soft-Switch's DAD architecture supports IBM PROFs, DEC's ALL-IN-1, VMSmail, and DECmail, Wang Office, MCI Mail, and Soft-Switch's own server that operates via SNADS; it can also connect to DISOSS, Wang Mailway, and a variety of PCs and word processors.

From Gateways to Backbone Networks

Soft-Switch's DAD spans the worlds of gateways and backbones. It basically allows a company to create its own backbone network of gateways that interlink different mail networks. By operating four DADs, for example, a company can interlink separate PROFs, DISOSS, Digital and Wang networks, as shown in Figure 12-8.

In Figure 12-8, the SNADS gateway is provided by Soft-Switch on a server product that can communicate with DISOSS, Wang Mailway, and specific word processors from NBI, Xerox, Wang, and IBM. As the reader can see,

Soft-Switch's DAD provides an immediate capability to interlink existing mail systems and networks. The major problem with the DAD concept, however, is that it requires the envelope of a message to be converted twice every time the message is routed to a different network, adding considerable overhead to all intersystem messages.

Figure 12-8. Interlinking Four Networks via DAD Gateways

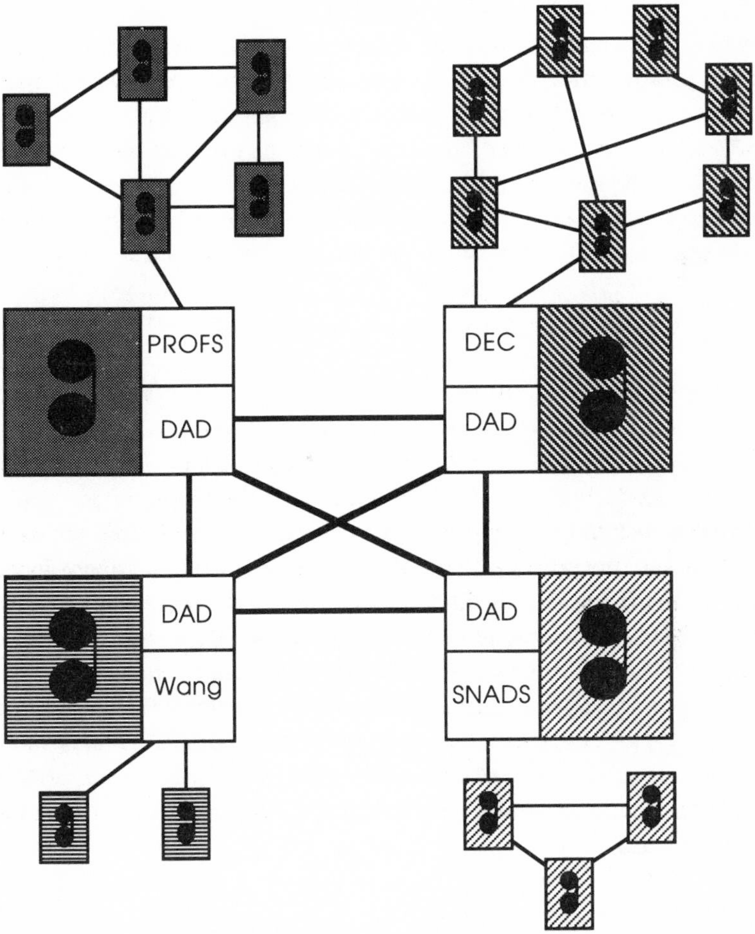

The DAD, however, is available for delivery immediately, which is its greatest advantage. It is designed as a short-term alternative until X.400 systems and IBM's SNADS are operating reliably in the market across a wide range of systems.

X.400's Gateway and Networking Advantages

Over the long-term, companies must look toward a mail architecture that is compatible with as large a number of primary mail systems as is possible in order to keep gateways to a minimum because of their high overhead and low throughput. This is where X.400 provides companies with both short-term and long-term advantages.

X.400 can operate as a gateway, as a peer-to-peer networking product, or as a backbone switching system. By the end of 1987, for example, there will be X.400 gateways on the market for most of the major private electronic mail systems, including DEC, Data General, Hewlett-Packard, Wang, Honeywell, and Unisys. Telenet and BT Dialcom will also have public X.400 gateways that will allow mail to be passed to private systems in different companies or between systems within one company.

These X.400 gateways will operate in the same manner as Soft-Switch's DAD. Each message must go through two envelope conversions. The major difference, however, is that all the mail systems from major vendors will also be converted to X.400 directly during the next few years so that companies will be able to replace their X.400 gateways with software that communicates directly without envelope conversions. In the long run, X.400 will give network planners maximum flexibility to set up their network in the most cost-effective manner possible.

Summary

The interconnection of mail systems, by its very nature, must be a slow, careful process. Because of the complexity of the task, there will be considerable overhead added to existing systems to handle functions such as envelope conversions and message transfer reliability, especially when gateways are used. The lack of a standard directory and network administration capabilities will also cause confusion. The bottom line, however, is that leading computer and telecommunication companies are now investing millions of dollars to interconnect their previously incompatible mail systems via both X.400 and SNADS. Telenet already has a conformance testing facility that will greatly aid vendors in making sure that the bugs are worked out as quickly as possible in their different implementations of X.400. Public services are also forming to provide intercompany X.400 communication services. Although the overall process of interconnecting mail systems will unquestionably take a few years, there are already numerous proprietary solutions on the market, and X.400 is around the corner. Now is the time to begin planning and implementing the interconnection of incompatible electronic mail systems and networks.

Planning and Implementing E-Mail

Although there are no formal rules as such for planning and implementing electronic mail systems, there are some sound principles that have evolved. If these are followed, the chances of a successful system are very high. The principles are:

- Take a global view of electronic mail's role in the organization, including its strategic applications and its relationship to other technologies;
- Develop an organization designed to integrate different technologies and bring users into the planning process;
- Consider all of the electronic mail technologies, not just the mailbox systems;
- Create a multidisciplinary team to plan and implement electronic mail;
- Implement with a phased approach that runs from a trial to a limited production system, to a full-scale corporate network;
- Look for users as high up in the organization's pyramid as possible;
- Keep operations as centralized as possible for proper technical control, but spread administration as widely as possible for the maximum reach;
- Develop tools to sell the system internally as if a public service were being sold to outside customers and then listen closely to their needs;
- Take advantage of the PC for easy access and training;
- Avoid line editors at all costs;
- Add non-direct users to the system via integration with mailroom printers and departmental secretaries; and
- Develop a strong accounting system for monitoring performance.

Take a Global View

The first step in implementing any mail system is to understand its global architecture. The reason is very simple. If you know where you are going, it is considerably easier to plot a course to get there. In the book *Planning For Integrated Office Systems*, Tapscott, Henderson, and Greenberg, write:

Many organizations remain somewhat myopic when for-
mulating office systems strategies and plans. Plans for word
processing and telephone systems are generally con-
structed with short-term objectives of cost displacement.
Often the same is true for data processing and even
management information systems. Many so-called
strategies have been developed in a vacuum without adequate consideration of the broader business context and
relevant issues. As a result, their impact on the organization
is often limited, or "tactical", rather than "strategic". Such
plans not only miss opportunities, but also poorly position the
organization to survive a period where technology is becoming critical to business success.[1]

It is very easy to talk about taking a global, strategic view of electronic mail
early on in the planning cycle. The realities of short-term user needs,
however, often make this a difficult and unpopular position within any organization. In electronic mail, however, the pain is relatively minimal because of the numerous alternatives available for meeting user needs. From
this perspective, taking a global, strategic view means:

- Actively understanding the strategic goals of the organization and planning applications that meet those goals as well as possible;
- Understanding how electronic mail fits into other developing technologies
  so that an integrated technology architecture can be developed;
- Identifying a global mail network architecture as soon as possible; and
- Meeting short-term needs as well as possible without sacrificing a long-
  term architecture.

Top-down strategic planning starts with the company's strategic plan. It
should be the cornerstone for all technology planning. The second step is
to take an inventory of technologies that exist, so that planners have the
best framework possible for plotting a future course. The next step is the
most difficult: *To use technology strategically, planners must adopt a
systems view toward applications because most strategic goals will require
a series of technologies in order for the goals to be met properly.*

Electronic mail, in short, is only a small part of the overall technology
picture. In practice, a CBMS must be integrated with data bases and bulletin boards in order for it to meet most systems applications. In addition,
text-based, ASCII messages are not enough to meet user needs. Documents, business forms, and other formatted files must also travel on the

system. As most CBMS on the market do not have all of these elements, electronic mail planners must work with other groups in the organization to develop these integrated systems.

One common type of development strategy is to build a shell for the host that integrates access to the various technology components via a menu. When users sign on to the shell, they can gain access to key data bases, bulletin boards, or electronic mail. PC front end software can tie the application together by allowing information received from one of the technologies to be captured on the PC and transferred to another technology. In this way it is possible for a user to check a price list in a bulletin board or inventory level from a data base and send the results to other users via the electronic mail system.

It is also important that planners identify their global mail architecture as soon as possible. If the company has multiple divisions in locations worldwide, for example, it will require a backbone electronic mail network to tie together the various systems that are already operating. Even medium-sized companies may require a backbone network if the firms plan to install numerous small LANs operating across the company. The company must also decide quickly whether the architecture will be based on X.400, IBM SNADS or another vendor's proprietary applications-level network protocol. This is a critical decision that should not be made hastily, although it must be made as early on as possible.

Even the smallest company should have some type of electronic mail architecture, although it certainly does not require the same level of resources and planning that is required by large companies. The company, however, should have a good idea of its short- and long-term needs and should plan accordingly. For example, if a small company decides to put an electronic mail system on its LAN, the choice of package might be influenced by long-term factors, such as the desire to communicate electronically with key customers and suppliers. Small companies with a need for telex may also find that their needs can be met by using a CBMS, such as Telemail, which has a real-time telex option. This saves the company the need to purchase a separate telex machine and dedicate an outside telex line. The same may be true for facsimile. If the company has a few PCs, one of them might be converted into a facsimile machine for about $1,000, depending upon the needs for facsimile.

Once the architecture is chosen, it is then possible to meet short-term needs without sacrificing a long-term integrated network. The two biggest problems that planners face in this area are the growing number of LANs that are being installed within various departments and the incompatible mail systems that already exist in different divisions or major departments. It is quite common to find a home-grown mail system running inside an engineering department, along with a number of mail systems in different divisions. Each LAN sprouting up will have its own electronic mail system for local users, along with the ability to gateway from the LAN to remote systems. How does a planner prevent a cacophony of different mail systems from developing, or take an existing cacophony and mold it into an integrated whole?

This is a difficult problem to solve in theory, let alone in practice. Without a guiding architecture, it becomes almost impossible to solve because there is no frame of reference for long-term decisions. With an architecture, planners can start attacking the problem right from the beginning. To use football terminology, a good offense is the best defense. In LANs, for example, central planning should take the lead in searching for a mail system that runs across many LANs and has the potential to be upgraded so that it functions as a node within the company's global architecture. When such a mail system is identified, central planning should make its use mandatory on LANs unless the department can identify a mail system that is also compatible with the chosen architecture. In this way central planning provides an immediate solution to LAN users, while at least opening the door for them to find an alternative that might better meet their local needs.

Solving the problem of existing systems that are incompatible is more difficult, especially when many of the systems have strong proponents with their own iconoclastic views. In general the best strategy is to convince the users to agree on some type of migration plan. In some cases, the software vendor will agree to develop the appropriate gateway. In other cases, users may agree to move to a new mail system if given an appropriate lead time, especially as they will not wish to be isolated inside their organization. The key for central planning is to provide education on the benefits of an integrated network, along with a working solution that does not sacrifice short-term needs.

Develop an Organization Designed for Integrated Planning

One of the most critical factors for any organization is having the proper structure to plan for integrated technologies. There should clearly be someone in the organization charged with overall responsibility for planning electronic mail. Today, however, it is common for electronic mail planning to be shared across MIS, telecommunications, and general administration. The same is true of other technologies. Even companies that have theoretically reorganized their technology planning often have done little more than consolidate separate departments under one V.P. or senior V.P., depending on their management structure.

Figure 13-1 shows an organization chart for a company's Information

Systems Division, designed to support integrated planning by the technology planning and implementation teams. This structure may be viewed as utopian by some, and, in fact, it is not mandatory that an organization restructure to properly plan integrated mail systems. Many organizations, however, are actively seeking strategies that will improve their planning. The chart in Figure 13-1 should be taken as a suggestion worth consideration, not as an imperative required for planning. Readers should also keep in mind that no matter how the organization is structured, cooperation is still the most important factor for success in planning and implementing any technology that cuts across organizational boundaries.

Figure 13-1 suggests some variations on the way in which most Information Systems operations are organized. First, technology planning should operate as an arm of the company's Executive Committee via a Technology Planning Committee chaired by the senior V.P. of Information Systems. The role of the Technology Planning Committee is to review the company's strategic technology plan, which should integrate with the company's overall strategic plan.

Second, all technology-related departments should report directly to the senior V.P. of Information Systems. The Telecommunications post has responsibility for all network operations, including both voice and data communications; the MIS post has responsibility for operating the main data centers and the host side of most network applications; the End User Computing post is responsible for personal computers, along with the evolution of word processing, dictation, and other centralized productivity tools offered as services to end user departments; and the Network Applications post is responsible for planning and non-technical implementation of communications-related applications, except, perhaps, for select remote data bases and existing remote batch computing applications.

The End User Computing and Network Applications posts are likely to be new at the V.P. level. They are important because they elevate the importance of PCs and network applications to the level they deserve within an organization. The End User Computing post should also centralize planning for the evolution of all end user application tools, and the Network Applications post should provide a focal point for planning all strategic applications that require integrating a variety of technology tools.

Although these positions are for a central planning organization, it should be kept in mind that as technologies disperse, central planning groups often become divorced from the operational realities of the organization. Thus, there is one amendment to this organization plan. The Technology Committee should have subgroups that work directly with the V.P.s of each line department to help in the planning and implementation process, ensuring that users have a strong input into the planning process so that their needs are represented.

Figure 13-1. Organization of Technology Planning Operations

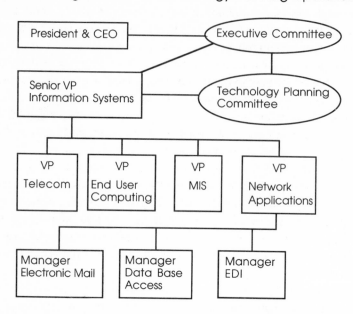

Study All Electronic Mail Technologies

Too many planners only think of electronic mail in terms of one technology— computer mailbox systems, which is a mistake. Although CBMS are the heart of electronic mail, there is a significant percentage of traffic that will benefit from transmission by other electronic mail technologies. This means that planners must take a close look at technologies such as facsimile, voice mail, and computer conferencing, in addition to computer mailbox systems.

Facsimile is particularly important now that its costs have dropped so low. It is quite likely that facsimile machines can be placed in major departments throughout an organization in much the same way that copiers were distributed 10 to 15 years ago. These fax machines can be cost justified largely by displacing the need for courier services. In addition, computer mailbox systems will soon be able to interconnect with today's facsimile machines, which can then serve as output devices to send messages to users who do not use the mailbox system.

Voice mail can also play a valuable role in organizations that have a substantial number of users who resist text-based mailbox systems. Although early voice mail systems were very expensive unless used by large numbers within an organization, it is now possible to deploy voice mail for one or two departments, such as sales and customer service, for a modest cost. Although voice mail systems are not likely to be compatible with text mail systems in the near future, they are so easy to use that there is little problem with a large number of mailboxes. Although it might be difficult for users to have several text-based mailboxes within an organization, there seems to be little problem with users having separate text and voice mailboxes.

Computer conferencing also has a role to play in electronic mail, particularly in organizations with sophisticated users. Computer conferencing is far better than electronic mail for planning-related applications because the messages are organized by subjects automatically, with a record created on each topic. In contrast, although electronic mail is effective for group communications, users must still keep their own files on a topic-by-topic basis; so, no consolidated record exists of all the communications.

Studying all the various electronic mail technologies does create two problems. First, few organizations are in a financial position to afford every technology that is available. This means that planners must prioritize their investments in electronic mail, spreading them over a number of years as required. This, of course, can only be done in relationship to the investments required for other technologies and for other business activities of the organization.

Second, responsibility for electronic mail is now spread throughout many departments within most organizations. Telex and voice mail are often controlled by the telecommunications department, and facsimile is split between telecommunications and administrative organizations. CBMS, however, are usually controlled by the MIS department. In order to receive a maximum return on investment, companies should have some centralized electronic mail planning function, even if the technical implementation, operation, and budgets are handled by other departments. If nothing else, the person in charge of electronic mail planning can play an important role by serving as a focal point for educating different departments about the benefits of various technologies.

Create a Multidisciplinary Team

Planning and implementing electronic mail requires a multidisciplinary team. It is a mistake to assign technically oriented employees alone to the task. Although systems engineering is a critical component to ensure reliability and proper operation, it is not sufficient if the implementation is to be as effective as possible. The team should consist of people with marketing, engineering, and customer service experience. Although it is obvious why engineering and customer service experience is required, marketing is equally as important. Although mail usage will spread on its own for elemental applications, the rate can be stimulated by an internal marketing campaign. In addition, a central planning team is often required to develop systems applications that integrate access to data bases, bulletin boards, and electronic mail.

Internal marketing, incidentally, does not mean hucksterism, although a little pizazz will not hurt. It means having someone who can carry out research into applications, put together an internal justification for the systems that are recommended, and develop an implementation plan that includes professional operations, training, administration, and marketing. Out of sight, out of mind is a truism that planners should heed. Although users may be convinced of the benefits of electronic mail, breaking old communication habits is a slow process. The more that can be done to make electronic mail systems visible so users know the systems are available for use, the higher will be the payback.

One problem is how to find someone with good marketing talents who is willing to work on implementing internal systems. If top management becomes committed to implementing advanced technologies, however, there is a ready solution. The company should transfer product managers from its sales and marketing operations into technology planning to help with the implementation of strategic technologies. Although this may be controversial initially, it makes sense to have personnel who are experienced with selling and planning products involved in implementing advanced technologies that require product planning skills. When people with these skills are put on a team with good system designers and implementers, the result should be a powerful combination. The transfers, of course, will be temporary, lasting perhaps one to two years.

Implement Systems with a Phased Approach

After any electronic mail systems are approved, they should be implemented using a phased approach with two or three stages: a trial, a limited production system, and a full-scale corporate network, if the organization is large enough to need it. For CBMS, which require the most careful implementation, most companies in North America have already moved into the second stage, although it does not hurt to explain all three stages.

The Trial Stage

The trial stage is used to see how a CBMS works for a relatively small group of users. Experience has shown that a trial should have at least 50 users and preferably 100 to 200. It is important in the trial to have a core group of users who are committed to using the system. It is also important to allow users to be added to the trial so that the company can get a feel for how the system spreads throughout the organization. But the most important part of a trial is a defined ending, along with an evaluation of the usage. It is not necessary to take out the system once the trial is over. This is usually impossible. It should be made very clear, however, that it is only a trial, not a production system, so that users know up front that a different production system may be implemented.

This is important because users tend to like the first mail system they learn and will be hesitant to move to another system. Many companies, have implemented a trial and met with a strong outcry when a different production system was chosen. This can be a real problem, especially if the trial system is not suited for long-term usage because it does not meet the standards of a long-term architecture.

Although trials are better suited for large and medium-sized companies, even small companies should distinguish between a production system and a trial. During a trial period, the small company is looking to meet basic needs. After the trial is over, the small company should then perform an evaluation of which service or system provides the most economic benefits. Frequently companies will spend a long time evaluating vendors when they do not even know what their final operating parameters will be. Unless the user knows exactly how the system will be used, it is best to set up a trial relatively quickly and leave the competitive evaluations until later so that such evaluations can be performed based on hard operating statistics.

Limited Production System

A limited production system is typically centralized on one of the company's mainframes or operated on a public service. Its main distinguishing features from a trial are that it has no defined ending point and that it also has formal procedures to add new users and bill-back departments, which is a wise idea. The best way to avoid the issue of the central planning group worrying about cost justifying each user is to pass the problem to each department manager. I remember, for example, an MIS director who discovered a production electronic mail system under his control without departmental bill-back. The MIS director put a freeze on adding new users until he could establish procedures for justifying its use. The hue and cry from the field was intense, and the company spent a few weeks in an internal war. The MIS director was likened to Darth Vader as the Force of Darkness, and he called a number of vociferous users a bunch of zealots. If each department manager must pay for the system from his or her budget, then a great deal of acrimony can be avoided. The only requirement is that the mail system must have an accompanying accounting system capable of departmental billing.

Corporate Network

The difference between a full-scale corporate network and a limited production system is its scope. A limited production system is usually based on software running on a central host, with the capability of growing from a few hundred to a few thousand total users. A full-scale network is designed to handle every user in the company, which may result in a jump from a few thousand to tens of thousands of users. The architecture that works well for a limited production system will not always work in a full-scale network. In most companies, for example, a full-scale network will require integrating multiple hosts into a multinode network.

Larger companies may also require a backbone network to route messages between separate nodes. A corporatewide mail network may also require handling electronic data interchange (EDI) and batch data files as well as mail messages. In short, a full-scale mail network is very different from a limited production system and requires a different planning framework.

Even if the company starts a production mail system with software that allows peer systems (the same mail software running on a different host) to pass messages to each other, it may not be sufficient to meet the needs of a full-scale corporate mail network. This is also a critical point that can confuse planners. As an example, although the software may be able to transfer messages to a peer system, does it have a directory of users that can operate across the network? Can it handle a wide variety of non-interactive traffic, such as EDI, internal forms, batch computer data, word processing documents, and other PC files? Can it operate as a backbone to minimize network communication costs? Does it have an architecture that is open to allow other mail systems to participate in the network?

Look for Users High Up in the Organization's Pyramid

When I was involved in my first electronic mail implementation in 1980, the operating wisdom was to secure approval from the top but to implement from the bottom. In retrospect, this is not the best way to implement electronic mail. Implementation should proceed from top to bottom if at all possible. Most organizations are hierarchical, with those at the top of the pyramid defining the appropriate forms of communications. If the CEO sends paper memos, then those down the line will send paper memos in return. If the CEO sends electronic mail messages, others in the organization will do so, too. The fastest way to get everyone in a company looking for electronic mail messages is to get the CEO to start sending them.

In practice it may not be easy to implement at the top because many executives will resist using new technologies themselves, even though they may support their usage by everyone else in the organization. One of the key goals of the planning team will be to get top executives and/or their secretaries using the system on a daily basis. This is an important point. Although top executives may themselves not use the system on a daily basis, it at least is possible to get the executives to have their secretaries send out memos electronically. This may lead to direct usage as soon as it becomes obvious that the system is easy to use, especially if it is accompanied with good PC front end software.

To make an electronic mail system appealing to top executives, it is usually necessary to provide more than electronic mail. Access to key operations data is also valuable. Thus, if the electronic mail planners work closely with those responsible for planning remote data bases, it may be possible to put together an executive information network that includes access to key operational data and electronic mail. To give one example, Canadian Pacific has an executive information system that allows any top manager access to up-to-the-minute operations data and historical data about CP's rail operations. The executives have keys with programmable ROMs (Read Only Memories) that unlock the terminals. The ROMs have the log-in routines to the integrated data base and mail system so that the executives only have to type in their passwords. They can then find out the status of every train in the network, including whether it is meeting its time schedule and what cargo it is carrying. It is also possible to compare periodic shipment figures with past figures.

Common thinking concerning implementing advanced technologies is that executives will not type. Although this may be true for a certain percentage of executives, I have long believed that executives refuse to type because they have no valid reason to learn. It is the planners, not top executives, who are often to blame. Most top executives, for example, do not require word processing because they have secretaries. They also do not require spreadsheets, etc., because their job is to review plans, not create them.

If, however, top executives had the ability to access key operations and planning data directly, through terminals that were easy to use, their willingness to "type" might increase considerably. *Planners should not hide behind the conventional wisdom that executives will not type. Instead, they should give the executives some good reasons to learn.*

Get Users Involved with the Planning

One of the most important parts of planning and implementing electronic mail is to get key users involved. The more that users are involved in the planning process, the more likely they are to be committed to any resulting system. Such commitment is critical during the planning stages before a trial, limited production system, or full-scale corporate network is implemented. There are a number of techniques that can be used.

The simplest is to make sure that users are consulted during all phases of the planning cycle. General users can be surveyed by questionnaire. Key users and managers can be visited, with their needs discussed face-to-face. This can be in single meetings or in focus groups, depending upon the size of the organization.

It is also a good idea to set up a formal user council, although it is not wise to impose much of a burden on these users, who also have their regular jobs to perform. The key point here is that consulting users goes a long way toward understanding their needs and assuring that they have a strong commitment to the success of any system that is implemented.

Centralize Operations; Spread Administration

Although the operations of a mail system or network should be as centralized as possible, its administration should be as decentralized as possible. Users and planners often confuse technical operation with administration. Operations includes maintaining the hardware and software and making sure that the system is properly backed up to provide file security. Administration includes signing on new users, providing departmental bill-back, training new users, handling user inquiries, and registering address lists and business forms. Although central planning may be able to field a team that provides basic services, such as training and registering select systemwide lists and forms, it is a mistake to keep most administrative tasks in centralized hands.

Departmental bill-back is a key issue here. As soon as the system can handle departmental bill-back, central planning can decentralize administration without being responsible for improper system usage. Instead, central planning can hold each department responsible for its own usage. Administrative tasks can then be passed to each department. In practice, this usually results in a secretary or administrative assistant assuming responsibility for registering new users inside his or her department and for handling administrative tasks associated with registering address lists and business forms, providing documentation to users, and handling basic user inquiries. Central planning can serve as a backstop to handle problems that cannot be resolved locally.

The benefits of departmental administration are fivefold. First, central planning can focus its efforts on planning, rather than on worrying about minute administrative details. Second, as responsibility for administration spreads throughout the organization, it creates a strong base of knowledgeable users who will help spread the word about the benefits of the system and also serve as an informal training network. Third, it provides planners with a ready-built information network to pass the word about new features, to serve as consultants to aid the development of PC front end software and additional enhancements, and to pass back information about usage, such as case studies of good applications. Fourth, it places administration as close to users as possible, allowing moves and changes to be entered into the system as soon as possible. This extends beyond names and passwords to the registration of group address lists and business forms, both of which require maintenance. A departmental secretary responsible for administering the mail system is unlikely to forget small details, such as updating address lists when people enter or leave the department or keeping forms up-to-date. In a centralized environment, these details are often lost. Fifth, it provides a base of trained users who can act as agents for non-direct users who may have IDs but do not have terminals or do not like to use the system themselves. These non-direct users are very important to the proper operation of a CBMS and are discussed later in this chapter.

Develop Internal Selling Tools, Then Listen

It is controversial to sell systems internally within an organization. Nevertheless, it is an important part of spreading use of electronic mail. Unless users know that mail systems exist, they will not use them. Internal selling does not mean hucksterism, but it does mean creating proper brochures that describe the benefits of the systems, providing a professional look to the group responsible for its planning and implementation, and taking active steps to promote the usage of the system.

To give some examples, internal selling means visiting key users and department managers face to face to explain the system and help the managers develop applications so that central planning avoids being viewed as part of some faceless bureaucracy that creates plans in a vacuum. It also means sending out brochures to users within the company to promote interest in the system and making sure that the system is publicized on a regular basis in company newsletters and other information sources. As the system evolves, for example, central planning should use its decentralized administration network as a source of case studies that can be published in the company newsletter or sent to a mailing list of department managers.

On all too many occasions, companies will spend $100,000-plus to set up a system and then not allocate a penny to let users know it exists. Instead, the company should allocate an adequate budget to prepare acceptable brochures on the system and to promote its usage.

Selling also means one more thing: listening. The best salesperson is the one who listens to customers' needs and then meets them. This is one of the reasons for bringing experienced marketing personnel on to the implementation team, if possible.

Take Advantage of the PC

Early electronic mail systems were developed for dumb terminals, and many companies still think of them in this way. Although the system may require access by dumb terminals, central planners should largely forget that they exist and focus on making usage as easy as possible for the growing base of PC users in the organization. This has two implications. First, an easy-to-use, PC-based front end program should be procured. If the mail system has one off the shelf, it is fine over the short term. Over the longer term, the company should consider using a third-generation package that allows for the integration of multiple applications, such as data base access, bulletin boards, and mail into a single application. (See Chapter 10.)

The goal is to emulate the online environment of the mail system as far as possible on the PC. If the company must develop its own program (or have one developed), this may cost the company about $10,000 to $20,000 above the cost of the software itself, but it is a small price to pay in medium-sized and large organizations if the front end package increases usage by 10 to 20 percent. A good front end might also decrease training time by one or two hours per user. If the system has 1,000 users who end up using the front-end package, this may save 2,000 hours of training time, which will more than offset its developmental cost. Small companies probably do not have the resources or the justification to develop their own interfaces. Instead, they should procure off-the-shelf software. In fact, a major decision point on which service to use is the availability of such software.

Second, the company can also develop a separate PC-based training program for users. The program does not have to be developed using a language such as BASIC, C, or Pascal. Instead, it can be a program such as the Bricklin Demo Program, which allows a PC to simulate how an application program operates. In fact, many of the vendors have realized this point and now provide such programs. To give one example of its benefits, GE Information Services provides both classroom and PC-based training programs for its Quik-Comm mail service. The cost differential is significant. To train a group of 100-200 people, training will average about $300 per user, whereas PC-based training will average about $70 per user.

Avoid Line Editors at All Costs

The single largest complaint about CBMS from users is that they must learn and use line editors. Central planners should not perpetuate the mistake of forcing line editors upon users unless they like relearning history. The best way to solve the problem is through a good PC front end package that has its own editor, although this does not always do the trick either. It is quite common for users to have simple means of creating messages offline on PCs, but no way to transmit the resulting message, except using X/on-X/off flow control, which does not check for transmission errors. The end result is that the user must enter the system's line editor to eliminate transmission errors.

Eliminating the need to use a line editor requires a means of creating messages offline and a means of transmitting the messages to the mail system without errors. This is one of the most difficult problems to solve because it is often beyond the planners' control. Although a PC front end can allow offline creation of messages, it cannot prevent errors unless the host has an error detection-correction protocol associated with basic mail messages. The only way to solve this problem is to put pressure on the host's software vendor to enhance the software.

Although the problem was unsolvable three years ago because PC software did not exist and the hardware had minimal capabilities to support advanced software, today there is no excuse for host software that does not provide support for an interactive error detection protocol such as X.PC. There is also no excuse for vendors not to provide good PC front end software. In the long run, if such protocols are not implemented, forcing users to learn line editors to correct line transmission errors, it will serve as a major deterrent to usage for a significant percentage of users.

Allow Non-Direct Users To Interact with the System

One of the most powerful ways to spread the CBMS throughout an organization is to allow non-direct users to interact with direct users. A non-direct user is someone who does not have a PC or a terminal. In today's environment this may include 90 percent or more of all white collar employees within a given company. If they are given IDs that identify them as non-direct users, it is possible for direct users to send them messages that are routed to a printer in the corporate mailroom, with the memo being delivered by the regular in-house mail system. These non-direct users can also go to any secretary on the system to send a message for them. This, of course, becomes an effective strategy to spread usage throughout the company. In addition, when the connection is made between the CBMS and mailrooms throughout the company, it also provides a strategy for solving the problem of infrequent users checking their mailboxes.

This is one of the most important features for a CBMS because its costs are minimal in comparison to its benefits, especially during the next decade as usage spreads throughout the company. This capability is also becoming a standard feature of most in-house CBMS software, although it should be a mandatory one as part of a buying decision. Planners who require this feature will almost certainly find top management more receptive to their plans to spread CBMS usage.

Develop a Strong Accounting System To Monitor Performance

The final planning and implementation principle is one of the most important: develop a strong accounting system. Such a system will prove valuable beyond its basic function of controlling mail system costs. It can also provide quantitative insight into whether the system is really improving productivity. One of the challenges to management is to develop an ongoing framework to evaluate the performance of the substantial investment that the company is making in advanced technologies. Most companies, for example, can compare their performance to competitors by studying comparative financial indicators. They can also study the performance of most products by internal accounting measurements. To date there are few companies, if any, who have developed a means to evaluate the impact of their advanced technologies in a quantitative fashion. The only way to start this process is to develop accounting systems that indicate how users interact with them.

The fact that accounting systems are in place does not mean that evaluation will be easy. Companies must also develop a new set of measurement techniques that can reflect accurately productivity improvement. To give an example, during the stage when technology is spreading throughout organizations, it may be possible to monitor the performance of users and non-users statistically so that one can compare telephone costs and courier delivery costs by department to see if statistical differences can be related to technology usage.

The purpose of these measurements is to provide tangible evidence that investments in technology are having a positive impact on the organization. In the final analysis, they may not be useful in proving productivity improvements. Good accounting, however, will be important to understanding and controlling the costs of technology — a significant achievement in itself.

Notes

Chapter 1 — The Challenge

1. Dean Meyer and Mary Boone, *The Information Edge* (Toronto: Gage, 1987), pp. 210-13. This book contains many case studies demonstrating how information technology improves operations, and offers a systematic approach to identifying the payback from using the technology.
2. I know these people personally but will not embarrass them by giving names in print.
3. Peter G.W. Keen, *Competing In Time* (Cambridge, Mass.: Ballinger Publishing Company, 1986), pp. 216-17.
4. These figures were supplied by Ken Bosomworth, president of International Resource Development, a well-known consulting firm in telecommunications and office information systems.

Chapter 2 — Benefits and Justification

1. I was directly involved as a consultant to the computer company in preparing the bid and can testify to the critical nature of the electronic mail system that was used.

Chapter 3 — Technology Overview

1. Ben Bagdikian, *The Information Machines* (New York: Harper & Row, 1971), pp. 28-32.
2. Trevor Housely, *Data Communications and Teleprocessing Systems* (Englewood, N.J.: Prentice-Hall, 1979), p. 16.
3. Daniel Costigan, *Electronic Delivery of Documents and Graphics* (New York: Van Nostrand Reinhold Co., 1978), p. 2.
4. Costigan, p. 3.
5. *EMMS* (July 11, 1987), p. 2.

6. Satellite Business Systems studied this phenomenon closely and designed a high powered facsimile-based system that could scan text and graphics and transmit at a rate of a page every one-half second to multiple locations. Its theory was to move electronic mail to the copier department, not to the word processing department. For a more detailed description, see *EMMS* (June 1, 1982), pp. 1-6.

7. For a detailed description of teletex, see Peter Vervest's excellent book on electronic mail, *Electronic Mail and Message Handling* (London: Frances Pinter, 1985). Vervest's book contains detailed descriptions of the CCITT's standardization efforts for teletex, facsimile, and computer-based message systems.

8. There have been numerous studies that estimate how managers and professionals spend their time. In general, about 15 to 30 percent is spent writing and on the telephone, and 30 to 50 percent is spent in meetings.

Chapter 4 — Communication Roadways

1. The leading suppliers of public CBMS services in North America are Western Union, Telenet, Dialcom, General Electric Information Services, MCI DISC, McDonnell-Douglas, CompuServe, Telecom Canada, CNCP Telecommunications, ADP Autonet, The Source, and Federal Express. Of these 12 suppliers, only Dialcom and The Source do not operate their own packet networks.

2. David Talley, *Basic Electronic Switching For Telephone Systems* (Rochelle Park, N.J.: Hayden Book Co., Inc., 1975), p. 13.

3. "Packet Switching Services & Equipment" (Norwalk, Conn.: International Resource Development, 1985), p. 26. I am also indebted to Dr. Vinton Cerf, who was directly involved in the early packet switching developments, for his insights into the early days of packet switching.

4. All the public packet network vendors publish lists of equipment that is approved for use on their packet networks. For more information, contact the packet network vendors directly.

Chapter 5 — Telematic Services

1. The CCITT develops standards recommendations for the telecommunications industry; its members consist of official government telecommunications agencies. Hardware manufacturers can participate in the work, but do not have formal voting capabilities. The CCITT itself works in four-year cycles and is organized by different

study groups that work on standards for both services and technical developments. Semantics also count. The CCITT, for example, does not set "standards", but instead makes "recommendations" (that end up having the force of standards). Key CCITT Study Groups for electronic mail include SG I, which works on international service recommendations; SG III, which works on international tariffs; SG VII, which is developing the X.400 message handling recommendations; and SG VIII, which is working on telematic services.

Chapter 8 — CBMS Applications, Costs, and Justification

1. I performed such an analysis in the September 1984 issue of *EMMS* newsletter (published by International Resource Development, Norwalk, Conn.).

Chapter 9 — Computer Conferencing

1. The results, published in the November 1, 1983, issue of *EMMS*, were consistent with other demographic studies carried out by The Source and CompuServe, although conferencing tends to attract a slightly more affluent group because of the resources required to spend hours online at about $8 to $10 per hour.
2. Thomas B. Cross, "Computer Teleconferencing: New Electronic Management," *Oxford Surveys in Information Technology*, Vol. 1 (1984), p. 220.
3. See Gerhard D. Wiebe, "Two Psychological Factors in Media Behavior," in *Mass Media & Society*, ed. Alan Wells (Palo Alto, Calif.: National Press Books, 1972), pp. 208-17.
4. *Ibid*, p. 208.
5. Starr Roxanne Hiltz, "Experiments and Experiences with Computerized Teleconferencing," *Emerging Office Systems*, eds. Landau, Bair and Siegman (Norwood, N.J.: Ablex Publishing Corp., 1982), p. 193.

Chapter 10 — PCs and E-Mail

1. Stephen Caswell, "Personal Messaging" in *Electronic Office: Management and Technology* (Pennsauken, N.J.: Auerbach Publishers, Inc., 1981).
2. The IRD report shows how fast PCs swept into our consciousness. In less than two years, they completely turned around the concept of how the electronic mail industry would develop. They also made the prediction in the earlier Auerbach article come true. By the mid-1980s, the cost of using electronic mail had dropped to about $500, which

included a modem and telecommunications software. Back then, however, we never envisioned that the PC would be that vehicle. We believed that electronic mail would be one of the driving forces for Office Automation. Instead, the opposite has happened. The PC, with word processing, spreadsheets, and other personal productivity programs, became the catalyst for CBMS.

3. Marshall McLuhan, Understanding Media (New York: McGraw-Hill, 1964), p. 8.

Chapter 11 — Voice Mail

1. Gordon Matthews is often called the father of voice mail and has had a distinguished career in telecommunications that includes developing Texas Instruments' (TI) text mail system, one of the first in-house corporate systems in the world. TI's mail system has now spread throughout the company. Matthews left TI to start a company called Action Communications, which produced the WATSBOX, one of the first low-cost routing telephone control systems on the market. He then sold Action to Honeywell, which gave him the funds to start up ECS.

2. *EMMS* (May 1, 1984) pp. 1-8.

3. The original version of this chart was supplied to *EMMS* by Rolm and published in the May 1, 1984 issue. Given that voice mail has become less expensive, although salaries continue to rise, the analysis makes voice even more cost-effective today.

4. *EMMS* (October 15, 1984), pp. 6-8.

Chapter 13 — Planning and Implementing E-Mail

1. D. Tapscott, et al, *Planning for Integrated Office Systems: A Strategic Approach* (Toronto: Holt, Rinehart and Winston, 1985), p. 47.

List of Acronyms

ADM	- Administrative Domain		**FCC**	- Federal Communications Commission
ADR	- Applied Data Research		**FDM**	- Frequency Division Multiplexing
ADS	- Audio Distribution System			
AOS	- Advanced Operating System (Data General product)		**FSC**	- Foreign Service Connection
API	- Application Program Interface		**IFIP**	- International Federation of Information Processors
CBMS	- Computer-based Message Systems		**IPM**	- Interpersonal Messaging
CCITT	- International Telephone & Telegraph Consultative Committee		**IRC**	- International Record Carrier
			ISDN	- Integrated Services Digital Network
CEO	- Comprehensive Electronic Office		**ISO**	- International Standards Organization
CICS	- Customer Information Control System (IBM product)		**IT**	- Information Technologies
COS	- Corporation for Open Systems		**LAN**	- Local Area Network
CRT	- Cathode Ray Tube		**LATA**	- Local Access Transportation Area
CWP	- Communicating Word Processor			
			MITI	- Ministry of Trade and Industry (Japan)
DAD	- DIU Assembler/Disassembler (see also DIU)		**MML**	- Man Machine Language
DARPA	- Defense Advanced Research Projects Agency		**MTA**	- Message Transfer Agent
			MTAE	- Message Transfer Agent Entity
DCA	- Document Content Architecture		**MTL**	- Message Transfer Level
DIA	- Document Control Architecture		**NBS**	- National Bureau of Standards
DID	- Direct-Inward-Dial			
DISOSS	- Distributed Office Support System		**OA**	- Office Automation
			OCR	- Optical Character Recognition
DIU	- Document Interchange Unit		**OEM**	- Original Equipment Manufacturer
EDI	- Electronic-data Interchange		**OSI**	- Open Systems Interconnection
EMA	- Electronic Mail Association			
EMMS	- Electronic Mail & Micro Systems		**PAD**	- Packet Assembler/Disassembler
ESI	- eMail System Interface		**PBX**	- Private Branch Exchange

PC	- Personal Computer	**SFD**	- Simple Formattable Document
PCM	- Pulse-code Modulated	**SNA**	- System Network Architecture
PMX	- Private Message Exchange	**SNADS**	- SNA Distribution Services
PRDM	- Private Domain		
PTTs	- Postal, Telephone and Telegraph authorities	**TDM**	- Time Division Multiplexing
		UA	- User Agent
RAM	- Random Access Memory	**UAE**	- User Agent Entity
RPOA	- Recognized Private Operating Agencies	**UAL**	- User Agent Layer
		USAM	- U.S. Automated Mail
		USPS	- U.S. Postal Service
SAA	- System Application Architecture	**VMX**	- Voice Mail Exchange
SBS	- Satellite Business Systems	**VTAM**	- Virtual Telecommunications Access Monitor
SDE	- Submission and Delivery Entity		

Index